W9-DES-037

Setting the Record Straight

The History and Evolution
of Women's Professional Achievement
in Engineering

Setting the Record Straight

The History and Evolution
of Women's Professional Achievement
in Engineering

Betty Reynolds, Ph.D.
Jill Tietjen, P.E.

white apple press
Denver

white apple press
1836 Blake St.
Denver, CO 80202
mailroom@penclay.com

Copyright 2001 by Betty Reynolds and Jill Tietjen. All rights reserved, including the right of reproduction in whole or in part in any form.

white apple press books are available at special discounts for reprint editions, bulk purchases, sales promotions, fund raising and educational purchases. Contact: Sales Department, white apple press, Finance Station, P.O. Box 480151, Denver, CO 80202; or: salesdepartment@penclay.com

Library of Congress Cataloging-in-Publication Data

CIP information is on file at the Library of Congress

Printed in the United States of America
Cover concept by Ellen Reindeau

*The paper in this book meets the guidelines for permanence and durability of the
Committee on Production Guidelines for Book Longevity
of the Council on Library Resources.*

∞

Printed on Recycled Paper

To Cassie and Ashlie

—Betty Reynolds, Ph.D.

With deepest gratitude to Alexis Swoboda, my dear friend and Society of Women Engineers' colleague, who planted the seed

—Jill S. Tietjen, P.E.

Contents

Foreword

In 1951, at the age of ten, when I said that I wanted to be an aeronautical engineer so I could build airplanes, I had no idea that this was an unpopular field for women. I found that out first in college, and then later during a 35-year career in the aerospace industry, where I was almost always the only woman in any meeting I attended. And I kept learning it all the way through my retirement from the Jet Propulsion Laboratory in 1998.

Information about engineers in a form understandable by (or interesting to) the non-engineer is rare. Rarer still is easily readable information about women engineers. *Setting the Record Straight: The History and Evolution of Women's Professional Acheivement in Engineering* will provide information for young men and women interested in the profession, and for the general public which often does not understand that engineers design and build almost everything we depend on in modern society. Many of these engineers are women.

I've talked to many thousands of people about projects I've been fortunate enough to work on—like robotic space flights to Mercury, Venus, Mars, Jupiter and Saturn. Many are surprised to find that while scientists collect the data delivered by radio from these distant worlds, it's mostly engineers who build and fly them.

Engineering itself is not only useful, but exciting. How can anything be more thrilling than seeing a picture from Mars of a robot that you helped design, trundling busily around the surface of another planet? What can be more rewarding than helping to build a tunnel under the English Channel or performing other, seemingly impossible feats to harness technology? Engineers design the systems that bring food and water to our burgeoning cities, and that take our waste products away. Engineers design the fetal monitors that contribute to a decreasing infant death rate and also design the factories and processes that create the drugs that prolong life at its end. Engineers design artificial parts of the body—pacemakers, artificial hearts, replacement joints and arterial stents. And engineers are behind most of the information technology that is driving the modern economy.

At the dawn of the 21st century, more and more engineers are women. The frantic pace of the modern, information-based economy has created a world-wide demand for engineers, and companies are realizing that there simply aren't enough white males to meet this demand. Much as the nation turned to "Rosie the Riveter" to build its planes and ships in the last global war, it's turning to women and other under-represented groups to build the underlying infrastructure for its new global economy.

At the University of Oklahoma (a fairly typical public university) where I'm Assistant Dean of Engineering (the first female Dean in the College's history), we are working hard to encourage women to enter engineering—and we're having a good deal of success. In fact, in one of our departments, Industrial Engineering, 40 percent of the faculty are women, and 52 percent of its students are women. Dr. Simin Pulat was just appointed the first female Director of a department in our college—not surprisingly, in Industrial Engineering. All but one of our departments have at least one female professor. This is just an example of what appears to be a trend in the U.S. It's a far cry from my college experience when there was *never* another woman in any of my engineering classes, and certainly no women professors.

A 1999 study on the characteristics of colleges which produce successful women graduates revealed that colleges that (among other attributes) have a critical mass of women—not only in the student body but on the faculty, on the Board of Trustees, and among the alumni—graduate women who go on to be more successful than colleges that don't have these characteristics.

Setting the Record Straight: The History and Evolution of Women's Professional Achievement in Engineering is a wonderful reference book for any woman (or man) who is considering the rewarding field of engineering, or for any parent with a bright and curious child—especially a daughter.

Donna Shirley
15 May 2001

Acknowledgements

As with any undertaking of this sort, many people provided support, assistance, and encouragement. We thank the following and apologize in advance for any errors or omissions.

From the Denver Public Library, Elena Wenzel. From the U.S. Department of Labor, Michael Williams. Eleanor Babco, from the CPST.

The accountants: Lynda Munion Dennis, CPA, Nancy Heimer, CPA, Cheryl Lehman, CPA, David Rediger, CPA.

The lawyers: Linda Bernard, J.D., LLM, Leslie Blau, Esq., Sally Lee Foley, Esq., Connie H. King, Esq., Dean Gail E. Sasnett, Janice L. Sperow, Esq., Heather Vargas, Esq.

The engineers: Dr. Mary Anderson-Rowland, Sherita Ceasar, Patricia L. Eng, P.E., Carrie Kessler, Rona Prufer, Sandra Scanlon, P.E., Dr. Margaret Wheatley.

From Women in Engineering Programs: Dr. Suzanne Brainard, Dr. Jane Daniels, Dr. Suzanne Laurich-McIntyre.

And other friends and supporters: Daylemarie Axtell, William Brentholz, Mary S. Dolan, Grace Fields, Dr. Frank Franco, Peggy L. Golden, Dr. Vance W. Grant, Kathy Grimm, Katherine Hager, Barbara Hirst, Phyllis Kopriva, Debby Lithgow, Ellen T. Mayer, Sue McGinley,

Albreta Merrit, Ramona Perry-Jones, Robert Polk, Sharon Madison Polk, Barbara Smith, Pat Snyder, and Professor Paula D. Thomas.

We'd also like to thank our publisher, Kendall Bohannon, and our editor, Wendy DuBow, at White Apple Press for believing in and supporting this series.

Betty Reynolds, Ph.D., Jill S. Tietjen, P.E.

INTRODUCTION

In 1998, a Harris Poll indicated that more than 60 percent of Americans knew little about engineers and engineering. Among the women polled, 75 percent knew anything about the field or its practitioners.[1] In light of this statistic, there's little wonder that recent congressional reports predict shortfalls of hundreds of thousands of engineering and technology professionals by 2010.[2]

Clearly there is—and will continue to be—a great need for engineers in our society, as progress demands more and different kinds of problem-solving knowledge and skills. And if trends in other traditionally male-dominated fields are any indication, women will be called upon to fill many of these positions. Historically, though, the field of engineering has been dreadfully slow in attracting, educating and retaining women. The first step toward rectifying this situation is to better understand just what an engineer does.

What is Engineering?

The field of engineering is vast, and the contributions of engineers are everywhere. Engineers help make the world a better place—from the clean water we drink; to the electricity that powers our homes and businesses; to the cars that we drive and the airplanes we fly; and, of course, to the computers that have enabled the information age.

An engineer is a person who has intensive preparation in the use of mathematics, chemistry, physics, and engineering sciences—including the principles of engineering analysis and design—and uses this knowledge to solve a wide range of problems and meet the needs of an ever-growing and ever-changing society. Engineers design, build, test, operate and maintain roads, bridges, rockets, power plants, cars, and refineries. The fields of focus in engineering are as diverse and numerous as our human needs. Indeed our development and progress as a society and culture is dependent upon the engineering expertise of aerospace and architectural engineers; chemical, civil, and computer engineers; electrical, industrial, and mechanical engineers; and, of course, nuclear engineers. (More information on the wide range of engineering fields is found in the Appendix.)

Women Engineers

Unfortunately, engineering has been the slowest of the traditionally male-dominated professions to accept women in its ranks. Only in the last quarter of the nineteenth century did women began to receive college training in engineering. Professional progress in the field has been extremely limited. The number of women receiving undergraduate engineering degrees finally reached one percent in the U.S. in 1972. Now, just after the dawn of the new millennium, it's estimated that female engineers make up slightly less than 10 percent of the engineering field. About 20 percent of undergraduate engineering degrees are awarded to women, whereas about 57 percent of all bachelor's degrees in all fields are currently awarded to women.[3]

The following table of bachelors degrees awarded in 1996 shows the percentage of women in engineering as compared to other fields:[4]

Field	Percentage of Women
Total all fields	55.15
Home economics	88.07
Library science	86.21
Health professions	81.64
Education	75.14
Psychology	72.96
Foreign languages	69.76
English language	65.97
Biological sciences	52.70
Mathematics	45.72
Architecture	36.06
Philosophy and religion	34.23
Theological studies	24.52
Engineering and engineering-related technologies	16.12

The field of engineering, for the most part, developed as the military's needs developed. Consequently, the field was virtually inaccessible to women. Women slowly gained access to engineering as the focus of progress changed from essentially military applications to society-building applications. The September 2000 report of *Land of Plenty*, issued by the Congressional Commission on the Advancement of Women and Minorities in Science, Engineering and Technology Development (CAWMSET), reports that women are not pursuing an engineering education today because of active discouragement; the dearth of out-of-school science, engineering, and technology experiences; lack of role models; social pressure resulting from the negative social image of scientists and engineers (which the report says is both inaccurate and derogatory); and lack of encouragement. Once in the engineering work force, women face inadequate work and family life accommodation, unequal pay scales and advancement, and non-inclusive behaviors in the work-place.[5]

In spite of these long-standing barriers, some women have successfully pursued engineering careers and have made significant contributions to the development of engineering. We know not only of their successes, but also of some of the hurdles placed in their way.

Lillian Moller Gilbreth, the "first lady of engineering" and one of the founders of the field of industrial engineering, was asked to speak at a meeting at the University Club in New York City in the 1920s. When she arrived in a cab, wearing her best evening dress, the attendant would not allow her into the building because she was female. She explained that she was the evening's speaker, but was nevertheless turned back into the rain where, of course, all of the cabs had disappeared. In a separate incident at the Engineer's Club—where women were usually allowed— Gilbreth was representing the Society of Industrial Engineers, but was asked to leave before the meal began, as women were not admitted to breakfast.[6]

Eleanor Baum, the first female dean of engineering at an engineering college in the United States, and the current Dean of the Albert Nerken School of Engineering at the Cooper Union in New York City, was not accepted at the first college to which she applied in the 1950s because they didn't have any women's restrooms. She was accepted at City College of New York where she was the only female studying engineering. Today, Dr. Baum is not only the first female dean of any engineering college in the U.S., but is the first female president of the American Society for Engineering Education.[7]

Despite the small number of women in engineering, and the often inhospitable environment in which they have to work, women have made and continue to make significant contributions to the field, and thus to our everyday lives. The story that follows chronicles their hardships and successes.

Chapter One
A SHORT HISTORY OF ENGINEERING

Although the formal profession of engineering originated in the fifteenth century as a military endeavor, scientific concepts applied in the form of engineering projects have been in existence for many thousands of years. The pyramids of ancient Egypt were begun as early as 2630 B.C. The Great Wall of China was built prior to 200 B.C. The Incas at Machu Picchu were excellent civil engineers. During 1450-1540, they designed extensive irrigation and other water-handling systems. The Rialto Bridge in Venice, Italy, crosses the Grand Canal and was built in the sixteenth century. Most of these early examples of engineering projects required a physical strength that, for the most part, only males possessed.[1]

Though few and far between, there have been female engineers throughout antiquity. Early women engineers and scientists include Tapputi-Belatekallim, an early chemical engineer and perfume maker in Babylon circa 1200 B.C.; Pythagoras's wife Theano (c. 500 B.C.), who ran the school after his death; botanist Artemisia of Caria; physicist and philosopher Arete of Crete; marine zoologist Pythias of Assos; Miriam the Alchemist (also called Mary or Maria) circa 200 B.C., who invented laboratory equipment, including the three-armed still and waterbath (still found in modern laboratories and known in French as *bain-marie* and in Spanish as *baño de Maria)*; and Hypatia (A.D. 370-415). One of the best remembered of the pagan women scientists, Hypatia invented the astrolabe (a device for measuring the positions of celestial bodies), an apparatus for distilling water, a hydrometer (a device for measuring the density of liquids), and a planisphere.[2]

When the term "engineering" first came into use, it described the design of mechanical devices for warfare. Universal scientific principles were applied, for example, in launching projectiles and determining approximately where they would land. The use of scientific principles, whose development was significantly enhanced during the Industrial Revolution, proved far superior to the previous methods, which were basically trial and error. Because of its birth in the military, women were automatically excluded from engineering.[3]

By the eighteenth century and the emergence of the Industrial Revolution, engineering moved away from purely military applications into the civilian sphere (hence the term "civil engineer") and began to resemble the various types of engineering we now know. This expansion was made possible by the realization that common principles applied not only to the building of catapults, but the building of roads and bridges, as well.[4]

Engineering continued to evolve as the physical world became better understood. Sir Isaac Newton (1642-1727) was led to his greatest discovery—the theory of gravity—by the fall of an apple in 1666. His theory is crucial to physics (a building block of engineering) and forms a key basis for mechanical engineering. His many discoveries affected virtually every area of the physical world, with special emphasis on experimental and theoretical physics, as well as chemistry and applied mathematics. Newton invented virtually the entire science of mechanics, and most of the science of optics. He also invented the mathematics he needed, including what is now known as calculus—a basic requirement for all engineering students.[5]

Using the mathematical foundation laid by Newton, other key principles underlying the various disciplines of engineering were discovered during the 1700s, 1800s, and into the 1900s. The Bernoulli equation, which described the motion of fluids, was developed around 1730. The law of electromagnetism, which describes magnetic forces exerted by electrical currents, was formulated in 1820. Many of the basic principles of thermodynamics came into being in the 1820s and 1830s, and precipitated the development and enhancement of steam engines. Electricity and electrical engineering was significantly advanced with electrical generation machinery (1884) and the transformer (1891), which allowed our system of electrical power to develop. Radioactivity was discovered in 1896 and the theory of relativity was put forth in 1905, allowing the development of nuclear power and a wide range of medical applications, including x-ray machines.[6]

At first, engineering resembled the craft traditions. Craft and merchant guilds in the thirteenth and fourteenth centuries had established rules for training apprentices to take over what were usually family businesses, and traditionally had welcomed daughters as apprentices and wives as unpaid artisans. Often women carried on the business in the case of a husband's death until a senior journeyman could take over. Sometimes she carried on the business herself indefinitely. However, once the fields that had traditionally been "crafts" were upgraded and transformed into "science," women were no longer welcome. In addition, the Industrial Revolution spawned mass production and increased demands for technical education. Mass production needed large numbers of engineers—apprenticeships did not turn out large numbers nor was it suitable for complex technical training. In addition, home-based crafts could not compete with mass production in price or quantity. As mass production took place in public, it became almost completely male. As in most other areas of life, the public sphere was dominated by men, while women were expected to exist in their own sphere, which was invariably personal, private, and domestic.[7]

Furthermore, as the discipline evolved, formal schools were established to teach engineering. European universities, however, did not admit women because of their heritage of being established to teach theology, medicine, and law. These professions were all closed to women. So women, with very few exceptions, were denied access to a university-level education. The École Nationale des Ponts et Chaussées (National

School of Bridges and Roads) was established in 1747 in France as the first formal school of engineering. In the nineteenth century, the practice and focus of engineering was significantly expanded with the development of Newtonian mechanics and the steam engine. These developments led to an even greater need for formal education.[8]

Male French engineers assisted the colonies during the American Revolution, stayed to construct the new nation, and provided the foundation of engineering faculty for the U.S. Military Academy (USMA) at West Point.[9] When it was established in 1802 to educate engineers, the USMA did not admit women. The Rensselaer Polytechnic Institute, established in 1824 in Troy, New York, now the oldest surviving non-military engineering school in the U.S., also did not admit women.[10] Despite the odds, a few women did manage to attend engineering schools. The first woman to graduate from an engineering degree program in the U.S. was Elizabeth Bragg, who completed a B.S. in civil engineering at the University of California at Berkeley in 1876.[11] Prior to the Civil War, there were only six schools of engineering across the entire U.S.; none admitted women.[12]

Elizabeth Bragg was a true pioneer woman in the field of engineering. In many professional fields, talking about the "pioneers" means talking about people who lived in the 1800s. In the field of engineering, however, many of the pioneering female engineers lived and worked in the 1900s. And, most of the earliest female engineers were not formally educated as engineers. Pioneering female engineers needed two advantages to achieve lasting recognition: outstanding achievements and strong personal ties with men in their field.[13] Close personal relationships with husbands, fathers, or other family members enabled women engineers to reach a level of professional acceptance that most other women were denied; it also gave them access to knowledge of particular fields.[14] Let's examine the history of engineering education for women in the early years of the U.S.

The 1700s

A young woman cannot and ought not to plunge with the obstinate and preserving strength of a man into scientific pursuits, so as to forget everything else. Only an entirely unwomanly young woman could try to become so thoroughly learned, in a man's sense of the term; and she would try in vain, for she has not the mental faculties of a man.

—Author unknown[15]

There is little historical data concerning women in engineering during the Colonial period in the U.S., possibly because there were so few of them and partially because the discipline itself was so young. Women who might have aspired to an engineering career were likely to come across a number of stumbling blocks, much the same as women in other male-dominated professions did. Chief among these stumbling blocks was a fundamental lack of access to formal education. However, the stereotypes about gender-appropriate occupations seem to have been even more sharply defined in science and engineering than in other fields.[16]

Engineering fits neatly within the traditionally prescribed masculine sphere of tough, rigorous, rational and unemotional work. These stereotypical male traits are the exact opposite of the ideal "feminine" stereotype at the time, and to some extent, even today: soft, delicate, emotional and non-competitive. This perceived polarity between the "masculine" nature of engineering and the "feminine" nature of women served as the perfect rationale to justify the exclusion of women from the profession for many years.

Further, exclusion of women from education—and particularly any type of higher education—fit with the mores of the Colonial period. The laws and customs that took hold first in the original thirteen colonies were based on English common law. According to English common law, women's social status was acquired either by birth or marriage. Women had many duties befitting their station but few, if any, rights; they were trapped in a condition known now as "civil death."[17] Women were deemed subordinate to men and were expected to play a subservient role, first to their fathers and then to their husbands.[18] Women's sphere was narrowly defined as domestic, and the female role specifically defined as wife and mother—roles later characterized as the "cult of true womanhood." Women were expected to be submissive and possess the values of piety, purity, and obedience. At this time in U.S. history, pursuing any form of rigorous education was considered inappropriate for women; they might harm their reproductive capabilities—especially if they filled their heads with radical ideas.[19]

While minority women were no doubt involved in some form of "science" and "technology" long before, during, and after the Colonial period, there is scant documentation to confirm their contributions. With the exception of limited reports of African-American women who engaged in medical practices on the plantations, there is little else to suggest that scientific pursuits were within the purview of minority women until long after the Civil War.[20]

The 1800s Prior to the Civil War

Education was not a widespread privilege (or requirement) for many years after our nation's founding. During Colonial times, education beyond the elementary level was denied to females. Formal education was rare, public schools as we know them today did not exist, and what education was available was not free. In fact, to be formally educated—especially beyond the high school level—was a rare privilege throughout most of Western history and exclusively granted to affluent males. When the Constitution was adopted, few colonials had attended school; the literacy rate for white women was about 40 percent, and for white men, about 80 percent.[21]

By the end of the eighteenth century, ideas about female education reform were beginning to draw attention. Judith Sargent Murray, an early advocate of educating women as well as men, protested the lack of equality in education between boys and girls in her 1790 tract *On the Equality of the Sexes*.[22] Female private schools, female seminaries or "dame schools," had begun to spring up in the 1780s, although attendance was usually limited to the well-to-do. Most of these schools focused on domestic subjects to ensure that their graduates would attract proper suitors.[23]

Women needed to lead the charge to ensure that education was available to women. Two of the more prominent of these women were Emma Willard and Mary Lyon. Credited with being the first person to make secondary education available for women, Emma Willard was able to inspire the citizens of Troy, New York, to raise enough money to build the Troy Female Seminary in 1821. More than anyone else, Willard wrought the basic revolution in the nation's attitude toward the education of women between 1819 and the 1830s.[24] Education reformer Mary Lyon established Mount Holyoke Seminary (later College) in 1837. She successfully endowed a school for women that not only exists today, but flourishes, and stands as a testament to her efforts.[25]

Also in 1837, Oberlin College set a milestone in education by becoming the first institution of higher education to admit women and students of all races. Oberlin had been established in 1833 as a seminary for men, but later became a college. Women were viewed as a "civilizing influence" on the men and, at first, were actually not allowed to take the same course load as their male colleagues due to their "smaller brains." By 1841, however, women were allowed to obtain the same bachelor's degrees with the same coursework as the men.[26]

During the 1840s through the 1860s (the so-called "Age of Reform"), women fought for change in many areas. During this period, female activists sought abolition, the right to vote, equal rights, and educational opportunities.[27] Soon, their efforts began to yield results.

By 1850, most cities had public schools—at least one for girls and several for boys. The state of education for minorities did not yet measure up to even these standards. And it took the better part of the nineteenth century to expand the free education system for males from elementary schools though high school. By 1860, there were only about 40 schools that qualified as high schools in the entire country.[28]

Colleges had been established as early as the 1600s in the Colonial states, and by the 1800s were fairly common in the eastern U.S. Young men had an opportunity to attend Harvard College and other Eastern all-male institutions. Although some of the early female seminaries called themselves "women's colleges," they did not measure up academically to these Eastern all-male institutions. However, they did lay the foundation for the establishment of Antioch in 1852, Vassar in 1865, Smith and Wellesley in 1875, and Bryn Mawr in 1885.[29] None of the women's colleges had an undergraduate engineering program.[30]

The picture was a little different in the Western U.S., where most colleges were state-supported and usually coeducational from the time of their founding because males were not enrolled in sufficient numbers to support them, and taxpayers would not support them unless their daughters could enroll. Many of these institutions came about as a result of the Morrill Act of 1862 that has been credited with democratizing higher education and providing colleges for the industrial classes. It also led to more schools that offered engineering education and more engineering programs open to women.[31] By 1870, Wisconsin, Michigan, Missouri, Iowa, Kansas, Indiana, Minnesota and California had established coeducational state universities. The number of women going to college increased dramatically between 1860 and 1920, as educational opportunities became available and women saw the economic and personal benefits of becoming educated.[32]

KEY HISTORICAL WOMEN

The number of women in science and engineering from antiquity through the Civil War for whom records survive is quite small. The contributions of these women are fascinating and in many cases, enduring. The following brief biographies provide a flavor of the lives they led, the accomplishments credited to them, and the difficulties they encountered.

Miriam the Alchemist (1st or 2nd century A.D.)

Born in Alexandria, Egypt, Miriam was also known as Mary, Maria, and Miriam the Prophetess or Miriam the Jewess. Her major inventions and improvements included the three-armed still or tribikos, the kerotakis, and the water bath. The original purpose of the inventions was to accelerate the process of metals transmuting into gold, but now they are used extensively in modern science and contemporary households. The tribikos was an apparatus for distillation, a process of heating and cooling that imitated processes in nature. Sponges formed a part of the mechanism and served as coolers. The kerotakis was an apparatus named for the triangular palette used by artists to keep their mixtures of wax and pigment hot. The water bath, also known as Marie's bath (*bain-marie*), is similar to the present-day double boiler.[33]

Hypatia (circa 360-415)

The daughter of Theon, a well-known mathematician in Alexandria, Egypt, Hypatia was raised by her father to be a "perfect human being"— in spite of the fact that she was a daughter and not a son. Raised to seek knowledge, she was educated in the arts, sciences, literature, philosophy, and all manner of sports. After her mathematical knowledge surpassed that of her father, she was sent to Athens to study. When she returned to Alexandria, she became a teacher of mathematics and philosophy. Hypatia wrote a number of treatises in algebra, including significant information on cones being divided by planes. Her inventions included a plane astrolabe, a device used for measuring the positions of the stars, plants and the sun, and to calculate time and the ascendant sign of the zodiac; an apparatus for distilling water, a process used for distilling sea water that is still used today; a graduated brass hydrometer for determining the specific gravity (density) of a liquid; and a hydroscope, a device used to observe objects that lie far below the surface of the water. Her brutal murder led to the end of the formal study of mathematics in Alexandria for over 1,000 years.[34]

Emilie de Breteuil du Châtelet (1706-1749)

The Marquise du Châtelet was tutored as a young woman because her parents thought her homeliness would preclude her being suitably married and wished to make her single life more tolerable with a good education. However, Emilie grew into a beautiful young woman of intelligence and wit who not only married, but had a well-known series of lovers, including a very long-standing relationship with Voltaire. Her significant intellectual interests were in physics and mathematics.

In collaboration with Voltaire, she wrote *Eléments de la Philosophie de Newton* (1738), which explained Newtonian physics for a French audience. *Institutions de physique*, published in 1940, originated as a physics textbook for her son and included principles from Newton and German mathematician Gottfried Leibniz. By now, students were arriving to study with Châtelet, and she began the culmination of her life's work, a two-volume translation of Newton's *Principia* into French. It was published in 1759, ten years after her death, which occurred a few days after the birth of her fourth child.[35]

Laura Bassi (1711-1778)

Laura Bassi, an Italian physicist, was fortunate to live in Bologna, Italy, a city that prided itself on being a leading center for women in education. At the age of 20, she was presented with membership in Bologna's Academy of Sciences, which was part of the Institute of Sciences. Shortly thereafter, she received a doctorate in philosophy from the University of Bologna. Although she was offered a chair in philosophy at the University and named a university professor, because she was a woman, she was allowed to give public lectures only by invitation. She was able to overcome significant resistance from various circles in Italian society as her career advanced via the support of her husband as well as members of the academic community, church leaders, and political figures.

She published scientific papers as a result of some of her research. Topics included: air pressure (1745), solutions for problems in hydraulics

(1757), the use of mathematics to solve trajectory problems (1757), and bubbles formed from liquids in gas containers (1791). Much of the rest of her research, which did not result in publications, involved fluid mechanics, Newtonian physics, and electricity. Because of her social position in Bologna society, she was also required to write poetry for community events and contribute to literary publications.[36]

Maria Gaetana Agnesi (1718-1799)

In 1748, Italian Maria Agnesi published a two-volume, 1,020-page manual titled *Analytical Institutions* that significantly enhanced the mathematical and scientific knowledge of the day. The volumes, intended as a textbook for her younger brothers, included analysis of finite quantities (algebra and geometry) in volume one, and differential and integral calculus (analysis of variable quantities and their rates of change) in volume two. Her clarification of the work of the best known mathematicians and scientists of the day, including Leibniz, Newton, Kepler, Galileo, and L'Hopital, was recognized for its importance around the world as translations were sought by scientists and mathematicians. All of this from a woman born in Milan, Italy, into a society where most young women, even in the upper classes, were not even taught to read.

The French Academy of Sciences described her work on infinitesimal analysis as "organized, clear, and precise," and authorized translation of her second volume from Italian into French in 1749. The English translation was published in 1801. In 1750, she was named honorary chair of mathematics and natural philosophy at the University of Bologna, although she never lectured. After her father's death in 1752, she gradually withdrew from mathematical and scientific activities, apparently because she associated those activities with him and the strong encouragement and support he had provided to her in her endeavors.[37]

Sophie Germain (1776-1831)

A young woman so determined to study mathematics that she persevered even after her parents made sure her bedroom was without light or fire and was left without clothes so that she would have to stay in bed, Sophie Germain was not allowed into the École Polytechnique at 18 years of age to continue her studies because she was a woman. Her parents had finally relented and allowed her to study mathematics during the day, and she was ready for more advanced education. Undeterred by the refusal of the École Polytechnique to admit her, she studied on her own through notes obtained from other students. She wrote to French mathematician Joseph Louis LaGrange under a pseudonym, and he was so impressed with her comments that he met with her and commended her observations. She later also communicated with German mathematician Carl Friedrich Gauss who was so impressed that, in 1831, he was successful in having the University of Göttingen award her an honorary degree.

In 1816, it happened that vibrations and their patterns was the subject of a competition for the French Academy of Sciences as the mathmatical theory to explain them had never successfully been developed. Germain's work, the only entry in the competition, was awarded the grand prize. The mathmatics for the vibration patterns are used in the construction of tall buildings, such as skyscrapers, today. Now that she had a prize, she was allowed to attend sessions of the Institut de France. In the 1820s, Germain became interested in number theory and developed a theorem in support of Fermat's last theorem, her most important work in number theory. Her theorem has since been generalized and improved, but not replaced.[38]

Mary Fairfax Somerville (1780-1872)

One of the first honorary women members of the Royal Astronomical Society (Great Britain), Mary Somerville was responsible for "popularizing" science—writing books and papers that explained science to general readers, many of them women. After spending a year at a boarding school when she was 10 years old, Mary developed a thirst for reading and arithmetic. She taught herself Latin, and then algebra, after seeing strange symbols in a ladies' fashion magazine. When her parents found out about her interest in mathematics, her father forbade her to study, worried that mental activity would harm her female body. After her first husband died and left her with a modest inheritance, she openly educated herself in trigonometry and astronomy. Most of her friends and family did not support her educational efforts.

Mary married her first cousin, Dr. William Somerville, and found someone to support her pursuits of educational and intellectual matters. In fact, William encouraged Mary to expand her studies beyond mathematics and astronomy to Greek, botany, and mineralogy. In 1834, she published *On the Connexion of the Physical Sciences* which presented a comprehensive picture of the latest research in the physical sciences. Her 1831 book, *Mechanism of the Heavens*, contributed to the modernization of English mathematics. Mary was occasionally criticized for her "unwomanly" pursuit of science. Nevertheless, she was referred to, both in England and abroad, as "the premier scientific lady of the ages."[39]

Ada Byron Lovelace (1815-1852)

The daughter of the English poet Lord George Byron, Ada Lovelace now has a computer language named (Ada) after her. A somewhat sickly child, Ada was tutored at home and was competent in mathematics, astronomy, Latin, and music by the age of 14. Totally enthralled by Charles Babbage's Difference Engine (an early computer concept), at 17 years old, Ada began studying differential equations. As proposed, his second machine, the analytical engine, could add, subtract, multiply, and divide directly and it would be programmed using punched cards, the same logical structure used by the first large-scale electronic digital computers in the twentieth century.

In 1842, the Italian engineer, L.F. Menabrea published a theoretical and practical description of Babbage's analytical engine. Ada translated this document, adding "notes" in the translation. Her notes constitute about three times the length of the original document and, as explained by Babbage, the two documents together show "That the whole of the development and operations of analysis are now capable of being executed by machinery." These notes include a recognition that the engine could be told what analysis to perform and how to perform it—the basis of computer software. Her notes were published in 1843 in *Taylor's Scientific Memoirs* under her initials, because although she wanted credit for her work, it was considered undignified for aristocratic women to publish under their own names. Ada Lovelace is considered to be the first person to describe computer programming.[40]

Chapter Two
ENGINEERING EDUCATION
OPENS UP FOR WOMEN

Engineering Education in the Nineteenth Century

Prior to the late 1800s, engineering education was available only to male students. While the U.S. population was centered in the East, the colleges in the West and mid-West formally admitted women earlier than East Coast institutions, primarily because many state-supported institutions were established as a result of the 1862 Morrill Act. But even then, the number of women formally studying engineering in the late 1800s were very few. For most women whose aspirations were inclined toward science or engineering, the educational system and associated opportunities would not be widely available until late in the twentieth century.

Some women were able to slip in through the cracks that were starting to show in the male-dominated bastions of engineering educational institutions, either as students enrolled in engineering curriculum or in related science curriculum. Many of the early women "engineers" were not educated as engineers in the sense one would expect today.

Ellen Henrietta Swallow Richards was one of these non-traditional engineers. Although she was not an engineer by training, she contributed much to the establishment of the forerunners of environmental and sanitary engineering and is credited as the woman who founded ecology and home economics. When she applied to the chemistry department at the Massachusetts Institute of Technology for a graduate degree in chemistry in 1870, she was not accepted because the department did not want its first graduate degree to go to a woman. She was not rejected, however (as she was at all the other universities where she had applied), but instead was allowed to enroll as a candidate for a second bachelor's degree. She was classified as a special student who did not have to pay tuition (she had already received a bachelor's degree from Vassar College). Richards did not know that MIT had admitted her without tuition so that they could deny she was officially enrolled, if anyone complained. She completed her work for a doctoral degree, but MIT refused to grant it to her. MIT did not formally admit women until 1878.[1]

Elizabeth Bragg became the first woman to obtain an engineering degree. She graduated in civil engineering from the University of California at Berkeley in 1876. Kate Gleason was the first woman to enter Cornell's Sibley College of Engineering in 1884, but did not stay to complete her studies, as she was called back to help the family business. Perhaps the second female engineer by education, Elmina Wilson graduated in 1892 from Iowa State College with a civil engineering degree and was the first female instructor at that school. In 1893, Bertha Lamme graduated from The Ohio State University with a degree in mechanical engineering with an emphasis in electricity. She was the first woman to graduate with a degree in a field other than civil or architectural engineering.[2]

When the Society for the Promotion of Engineering Education (later named the American Society for Engineering Education) was formed in 1893, only the three women noted above were recorded as having received engineering degrees in the U.S. However, as women began to enter the educational system, graduate, and then try to find work as engineers, a backlash developed.[3]

Professionalization

Professionalization of engineering began in the late nineteenth and early twentieth centuries. As women were finally able, at least in small numbers, to gain an engineering education and engineering employment, they also endeavored to join the engineering societies. These organizations, however, did not welcome women and developed a strict hierarchy of requirements for each of several levels of membership. They were already in the midst of upgrading themselves and the entrance of women into the profession was not seen as a positive development by most of the men in the leadership positions of these organizations.[4]

Professionalization, in this case, meant upgrading the membership or image of a profession by excluding or diminishing the influence of persons who could be perceived to be "amateurs." Professionalization in engineering included deliberately creating barriers between engineers with college degrees and relevant professional experience and those other "engineers" who had learned their jobs by experience and lacked "professional" credentials. In professional societies, professionalization often meant raising the standards of membership and led to great concerns about the perceived prestige of the organization. As most engineering schools did not admit women (and thus women could not get the desired "professional" credentials), the most significant impact of professionalization was to exclude women.[5]

Professionalization was probably also a by-product of the state of engineering education. Engineering educational standards in the late 1800s and early 1900s were not yet at a level necessary to earn a college education. As a consequence, engineers were not invited to serve on national scientific advisory boards, nor were engineers recognized as part of the established scientific community until 1916. And not until 1932 was the Engineering Council for Professional Development (ECPD), now known as the Accreditation Board for Engineering and Technology (ABET), created to provide accreditation of engineering degree programs, in partial response to reports sponsored by the engineering societies.[6]

Professional Societies

By the end of the nineteenth century, civil and mechanical engineering were firmly established as engineering disciplines, with electrical and chemical engineering following closely behind.[7] Engineering societies were forming. Organizations, such as these engineering societies, are deemed the hallmark of a profession. These societies define intellectual style and norms of conduct and generally act to promote the interests of their members. The early engineering societies placed a high value on free enterprise, individualism, hard work, ambition, and success—characteristics of a rugged male culture, with concepts of prestige, status, and professionalism closely intertwined with masculinity.[8]

The "Founder" societies, the five original engineering societies that founded the United Engineering Society in 1904 (which later became the United Engineering Foundation) included the American Society of Civil Engineers (ASCE), the American Institute of Mining Engineers (AIME) (now called the American Institute of Mining, Metallurgical, and Petroleum Engineers), the American Society of Mechanical Engineers (ASME), the American Institute of Electrical Engineers (AIEE—a predecessor organization to the Institute of Electrical and Electronics Engineers—IEEE), and the American Institute of Chemical Engineers (AIChE).[9] A brief look at their history and their admittance (or more accurately, their lack of admittance) of women shows the impact that professionalization and the associated membership requirements had on the recognition for and advancement of women in the engineering profession.

ASCE, America's oldest national engineering society, was founded in 1852. Twelve founders met at the Croton Aqueduct in New York City on November 5, 1852, and agreed to incorporate as the American Society of Civil Engineers and Architects (later the ASCE). Emily Warren Roebling, probably the first female field engineer, became the first woman to address the ASCE in 1892, when she argued that her husband should not be replaced as the formal director for the construction of the Brooklyn Bridge. In 1909, Nora Blatch de Forest, a graduate of Cornell University in the top five of her class, was admitted as a "junior member" of the ASCE but was unable to advance any higher. When her junior membership expired in 1916, ASCE refused to promote her to full membership, in spite of her meeting the stated requirements. Instead, they dropped her from the rolls. She brought a lawsuit against the Society, but did not prevail. Elsie Eaves became an associate member of ASCE in 1927 and later, the first female member (1957), first female life member, first female Fellow, and the first woman elected to honorary membership (1979).[10]

AIME was founded in 1871 by 22 mining engineers in Wilkes-Barre, Pennsylvania. The first woman member was Ellen Henrietta Swallow Richards, who became the first female member of any engineering society when she was elected a full member of AIME in 1879. Richards was aided by her MIT degree, her publications in mineral chemistry, and the fact that her husband was vice president of the organization. In 1917, the Woman's Auxiliary to the AIME was established and is still active today.[11]

By 1880, 85 engineering colleges had been established in the U.S., and most offered a full mechanical engineering curriculum. Thirty engineers met in New York City in February 1880 and decided to form the ASME. In April, a formal organizational meeting was held with 80 engineers at the Stevens Institute of Technology in Hoboken, New Jersey. The first annual meeting of the organization was held in November 1880. The first woman member, Kate Gleason, was admitted to full membership of the ASME in 1914. Lydia Weld, a 1903 naval architecture graduate of MIT, became an associate member of ASME in 1915. She was allowed to become a full member in 1935, when the ASME finally granted full membership status to women.[12]

By 1884, twenty-five prominent figures in electrical technology signed a "call" to establish an American electrical national society, mindful that civil, mining, and mechanical engineers had already established their own national societies. Twenty-five electrical engineering practitioners met in the headquarters of the ASCE on April 15 to devise an organizational structure for what became at first the AIEE. The first general meeting was held on May 13, also at ASCE headquarters. In 1926,

Edith Clarke, who would later become one of the first AIEE female fellows, was the first woman to address the AIEE. As late as 1942, there were only three women in the AIEE and over 17,000 men. The Fellow grade was established in 1912 for engineers who had demonstrated outstanding proficiency and had achieved distinction in their profession. It was not until 1948, however, that the first women were elected AIEE Fellows. These three distinguished women were Edith Clarke, who significantly contributed to knowledge about and modeling for electric utility systems; Vivien Kellems, the founder of Kellems Company, a manufacturer of cable grips and shell lifters; and Mabel Rockwell, who significantly contributed to electrical control systems.[13]

AIChE was founded in 1908 at the Engineers' Club in Philadelphia by 19 men. Chemical engineering was just coming into its own and was somewhere between chemistry and mechanical engineering. The founding of AIChE helped to establish chemical engineering as a separate discipline. At the time, the founding members of AIChE believed that about 500 people were practicing chemical engineering across the country. The first female member of AIChE was Margaret Hutchinson Rosseau, the first woman to receive a Sc.D. in chemical engineering from MIT, and who made significant contributions to the field, was not admitted until 1945.[14]

In addition to the Founder Societies, an engineering honor society, Tau Beta Pi, was established. The engineering equivalent of Phi Beta Kappa (which had been founded at the College of William and Mary in 1776), Tau Beta Pi, was established at Lehigh University in 1885. It was founded to:

> ...mark in a fitting manner those who have conferred honor upon their alma mater by distinguished scholarship and exemplary character as undergraduates in engineering, or by their attainments as alumni in the field of engineering, and to foster a spirit of liberal culture in engineering colleges.

Membership in Tau Beta Pi was limited to men until 1969. Women's badges had been authorized in 1936 as an alternative to membership for women. Only 619 women's badges had been awarded by 98 chapters until women were admitted to full membership in 1969, 84 years after the founding of the organization.[15]

Other engineering societies, in addition to the founder societies, came into existence in the early to mid 1900s. However, these organizations also excluded women from membership or often relegated them to lower membership status. Marie Luhring was elected as an associate member of the American Society of Automotive Engineers in 1920. That same year, Ethel H. Bailey became the first full female member of the organization.[16] The American Society of Safety Engineers, founded in 1911 in New York City with 62 members as the United Society of Casualty Inspectors, admitted its first female member, Vera Burford, in 1946.[17] The first time a woman was elected as a junior member of the Society of Naval Architects and Marine Engineers was 1946.[18] The first female fellow of the Illuminating Engineering Society, Gertrude Rand, a researcher on the way color perception is affected by illumination and on color blindness, was elected in 1954.[19]

Lillian Gilbreth, "the first lady of engineering" and the co-founder of the field of industrial engineering, was made an honorary member of the Society of Industrial Engineers in 1921 (as a personal favor to her husband, Frank Gilbreth), but not admitted to regular membership. She was, however, the first woman elected to the National Academy of Engineering (NAE), an event that occurred in 1965, only one year after the founding of the NAE in 1964.[20]

Early Twentieth Century

The struggle for women to enter the engineering profession made some progress in the early twentieth century. Women are known to have graduated in engineering from some universities, even if only in ones or twos. Finding a job was the next problem. Attaining the credentials necessary for recognition as even a junior or associate member of one of the professional engineering societies was a further obstacle faced by most women. And then, if a woman married, she was expected, except in very rare cases, to become a wife and mother and abandon all thoughts of a career. The situation was so dire that *American Men of Science*, 1921 edition, lists zero women as employed in engineering.[21] The 1920 census, however, reports that of 130,000 engineers counted, 41 were women, up from 21 in the 1890 census.[22]

KEY WOMEN OF THIS PERIOD

The key women in engineering, whose most significant contributions occurred after the Civil War and prior to World War I, were generally not educated in "engineering." With admission to engineering programs prohibited for women in almost every instance, most of the women who impacted the engineering profession either were educated in other scientific fields or gleaned their "engineering" knowledge through on-the-job training.

Ellen Henrietta Swallow Richards (1842 – 1911)

Ellen Swallow was admitted to MIT as a "special student" and earned a bachelor's degree there in chemistry in 1873 (the first woman graduate of MIT) after having graduated from Vassar (as one of its first graduates) in 1870. She was denied an earned doctoral degree from MIT, as the school did not want a woman to be the first person awarded a doctorate in chemistry. While a graduate student, she executed a complete survey of Massachusetts drinking water and sewage for the Massachusetts Board of Health (1872), taking more than 40,000 samples. Through this work, she warned of early inland water pollution. She also contributed the first Water Purity Tables and the first state water quality standards in the U.S. From 1873 to 1878, she taught in the MIT chemistry department without a title or salary as the first women teacher. She also did extensive research in mineral analysis.

After her marriage in 1875 to Professor Robert H. Richards, head of the department of mining engineering at MIT, she persuaded the Women's Education Association of Boston to contribute the funds needed for the opening of a Woman's Laboratory at MIT. As assistant director to Professor John M. Ordway, an industrial chemist, Richards began her work in the laboratory by encouraging women to enter the sciences and to provide scientific training to women. In 1879, she became the first female member of the American Institute of Mining Engineers. She was certainly technically qualified for this membership classification; however her husband's status of vice president of the organization contributed significantly to her selection.

By 1883, the laboratory had proved so successful that MIT allowed women to enroll in regular classes and closed the laboratory. Richards' work in the laboratory had resulted in several books and pamphlets, including the seminal *Food Materials and Their Adulterations* (1885). This publication influenced the passage of the first Pure Food and Drug Act in Massachusetts. Her work included analysis of air, water, and food, and led to national public health standards and the new disciplines of sanitary engineering and nutrition. The interaction between people and their environment, her areas of study, have led to Richards being called the founder of ecology.

In 1884, she was instrumental in setting up the world's first laboratory for studying sanitary chemistry. She served as assistant to Professor William R. Nichols in the new laboratory and held the post of instructor on the MIT faculty for the rest of her life. From 1887 to 1889 she supervised a highly influential survey of Massachusetts inland waters.

Since 1876, Richards had been on the forefront of promoting education for women, especially in science. In 1881, Richards helped found the Association of Collegiate Alumnae (later renamed the American Association of University Women). In 1882, she helped to organize the science section of the Society to Encourage Studies at Home.

After 1890, she concentrated most of her efforts on founding and promoting the home economics movement (at first it was called domestic science)—an achievement for which she is primarily noted (and frequently criticized for its detrimental effect on women's equality). Home economics was given definition by a series of conferences held in Lake Placid, New York, organized and chaired by Richards starting in 1899. She was involved in the formation of the American Home Economics Assocation (1908) and was appointed in 1910 to the National Education Association.[23]

Emily Warren Roebling (1844 – 1903)

Emily Warren Roebling, generally considered the first U.S. female field civil engineer and construction manager, is remembered for her significant accomplishments in the construction of the Brooklyn Bridge. The inscription on the East Tower of the bridge (placed there in 1953) reads:

The Builders of the Bridge
Dedicated to the Memory of
Emily Warren Roebling
1843-1903
whose faith and courage helped her stricken husband
Col. Washington A. Roebling, C.E.
1837-1926
complete the construction of this bridge
from the plans of his father
John A. Roebling, C.E.
1806-1869 who gave his life to the bridge

"BACK OF EVERY GREAT WORK WE CAN FIND
THE SELF-SACRIFICING DEVOTION OF A
WOMAN"

Without Emily Warren Roebling, the Brooklyn Bridge—one of the greatest engineering projects of the nineteenth century—might not have been completed on May 24, 1883. With the assistance of her brother and husband, Roebling learned engineering through the study of higher mathematics, strength of materials, stress analysis, the calculation of catenary curves, bridge specifications, and the intricacies of cable construction. Her engineering skills allowed her to become the principal assistant and inspector of the bridge as her husband, Washington Roebling, could no longer visit the site because he had "Bends" disease. She was able to discuss structural steel requirements with representatives from steel mills and assisted them with designs and shapes never before fabricated.

She said, "...I have more brains, common sense, and know-how generally than any two engineers, civil or uncivil, that I have ever met..." The bridge, with a span of 1,595 feet, was the largest suspension bridge in the world when it was completed and remains functional today.[24]

Edith Judith Griswold (1863 – date of death not known)

Renowned as a lawyer and patent expert (this is how she is listed in the *Who's Who in Engineering* in 1925), Edith Grisworld spent four years at New York Normal College where she graduated with a license to teach in the New York Schools. However, she took a special course in electricity at the time (with her father's permission). She felt that she gained a great deal in the course, and that her best work was always along electrical lines.

Her career as a mechanical draftsperson began in 1884. In 1885 and 1886, she worked in D.J. Miller's office, one of the first cable railroad men, where she made drawings for and estimated costs associated with cable railroads. All of her subsequent work was in patent-office drawing. During this time, she also taught geometry and mathematics in a private school.

By 1887, she was very interested in patent law and gave up her work as a mechanical draftsperson to work as a managing clerk in a patent law office and learn the profession. She attended lectures at New York

University Law School. In 1897, Griswold opened her own law offices as a patent attorney. She took the bar in 1898. After 1905, her health forced her to give up regular office work.

Her engineering work was primarily in mechanics, including electrical apparatus, instruments of precision, and other intricate devices. Her legal work, which came from other patent lawyers, was always (with but one exception) patents related to articles used or worn by women.[25]

Kate Gleason (1865 – 1933)

Kate Gleason began her career in the family's Gleason Works at age 11 when her brother, Tom, died. Hearing her father lament the loss of his assistant, Kate simply showed up and took his place. And, her father did not send her back home to do "women's" things; he taught her the family business. By age 14, she was the Gleason Works bookkeeper. She became her father's indispensable assistant. In addition to keeping the books, she traveled around the country and the world selling the company's products, and serving as the public face of Gleason Works.

In 1884, she entered Cornell University's engineering program, the first woman to enroll. However, before her freshman year was over, she needed to return to the family business, as her father could not afford the salary of the man that had been hired to take her place. Although, she significantly lamented the loss of education, she was on the road by 1888, selling machines on her first road trip. By 1890, she was the Secretary-Treasurer of The Gleason Works, and its chief sales representative, a position she held until 1913. In 1893, on doctor's orders for rest, she went to England, Scotland, France, and Germany, and came back with machine orders. This was one of the earliest efforts at international marketing for any company in the U.S. Gleason learned how to turn being a female in business into an asset. She had also learned from Susan B. Anthony, one of the leaders of the suffragette movement, that any advertising is good. In 1913, family tensions, caused in large part by her being a woman in a man's world and to a widely circulated story that credited her with being the inventor of the Gleason gear planer (the inventor was her father), led to her resigning from the company.

Kate Gleason became the first female member of the ASME in 1914. Also in 1914, she was the first woman to be appointed receiver by a bankruptcy court. She successfully undertook the reorganization of the Ingel Machine Company of East Rochester, New York. In 1916, she was one of the first women to be elected to the Rochester Chamber of Commerce and the first woman elected to the Rochester Engineering Society. She also served as president of the First National Bank, Rochester, New York, from 1917 to 1919, while its president went off to fight in World War I.

Later, Gleason became very interested in low-cost housing and built concrete houses in the Rochester area that are still inhabited today. She was the first female member of the American Concrete Institute. Gleason served as the ASME's representative to the World Power Conference in Germany in 1930. Her estate was used to establish the Kate Gleason fund, one of whose beneficiaries was the Rochester Institute of Technology (RIT). In 1998, RIT named its College of Engineering after her. Gleason attributed her success to "a bold front, a willingness to risk more than the crowd, determination, some common sense, and plenty of hard work."[26]

Bertha Lamme (1869-1954)

Bertha Lamme went to work for Westinghouse after graduating from The Ohio State University with a degree in mechanical engineering and an emphasis in electricity. She had studied electrical engineering with her brother at Ohio State "for the fun of it," and had no plans to pursue a career after earning her degree in 1893. However, she received a surprise job offer from Westinghouse where her brother Benjamin was employed, and worked there until she married in 1905.

Bertha Lamme worked in the East Pittsburgh plant for 12 years, where she designed motors and generators. A 1907 *Pittsburgh Dispatch* article reports on her tenure at Westinghouse, saying that Lamme's work in designing dynamos and motors won her a reputation "even in that hot-house of gifted electricians and inventors. She is accounted a master of the slide rule and can untangle the most intricate problems in ohms and amperes as easily and quickly as any expert man in the shop."

In 1905, she married her supervisor and retired, as required by com-pany policy, to become a wife and mother. Her husband, Russell S. Feicht, also an Ohio State graduate, designed the 2,000-horsepower induction motors displayed at the St. Louis World's Fair in 1904, and later retired from Westinghouse as its director of engineering. The Feicht's daughter, Florence, had well-developed mathematical abilities and went on to become a physicist for the U.S. Bureau of Mines.

The Westinghouse/Bertha Lamme Scholarships were established by the Society of Women Engineers (SWE) in 1973 in honor of Westinghouse's first woman engineer.[27]

Nora Stanton Blatch de Forest Barney (1883-1971)

Nora Stanton de Forest Barney, granddaughter of Elizabeth Cady Stanton (one of the leaders of the suffrage movement), first distinguished herself by graduating from Cornell University with a bachelor's of civil engineer-ing in 1905. The American Bridge Company employed her, as she was in the top five of her class and a member of Sigma Pi. She became a "squad boss" after three weeks of employment. In 1906, she became an assistant to Lee de Forest, inventor of the radio vacuum tube and pioneer in tele-vision. They were married in 1908 and divorced in 1912. In 1909, she joined the staff of Radley Steel Construction Company as an assistant engineer and chief drafter. From 1909 to 1917, she was also active in the New York State women's suffrage movement. Then, beginning in 1912, she was an assistant engineer for the New York Public Service Commission. She married Morgan Barney, a marine architect in 1919. Barney also served as an architect and engineering inspector for the Public Works Administration in Connecticut and Rhode Island.

Besides her broad work experience, Barney was a prolific, and wide-ly read writer in her field. She was actively involved in the world peace movement and the women's rights movement. Despite her many achievements, she was granted only a junior membership status in the ASCE in 1909. Nearly 14 years after being allowed to join, she filed to have her membership status elevated to "associate member," but her application was denied. She filed an appeal, but her appeal was denied. And when she attempted to regain her junior membership status, it too was denied. In her later life she became a real estate developer. In 1944, she wrote *World Peace Through a Peoples Parliament.*[28]

Chapter Three
WAR'S UNINTENDED CONSEQUENCES

World War I

During World War I, women were encouraged to participate in the work force and support the war effort. The "war to end all wars" had also been called the first engineers' war, as the results of military applications of scientific and technological advances appeared as tanks, airplanes, and submarines.[1] Because of the shortage of male engineers during World War I, women had the opportunity to work in factories and offices where they were instrumental in keeping the manufacturing industry working.[2] They were drawn into tool design and chemical research, and designed buildings and automobiles.[3]

However, because the U.S. was involved in the conflict for only 19 months, the manpower emphasis was on the emergency training of mechanics to service the new military technology, and not the education of engineers with degrees.[4] Some women became war-time mechanics through special training; some of those women, because of this introduction, actually graduated with engineering degrees in the 1920s. Approximately 120 women, some without any college degree, worked during the war in engineering jobs. The end of the war signaled the end of this opportunity. However, prior to 1920, at least 45 women are known to have graduated from college with engineering degrees.[5] It is ironic that war, an activity that historically women tend to oppose, increases women's economic progress, just because men are drawn out of the civilian work force.[6]

Many historians believe that the vote for women's suffrage, which was finally ratified in 1920, was out of gratitude for women's efforts during the war.[7] However, in spite of that "gratitude," most women were not allowed to keep the jobs they had filled during the war when it was over. The few women who did remain in engineering after World War I must have been nearly invisible, because according to the *American Men of Science* directory for 1921, there were no women at all in engineering, although the 1920 census reported 41 women out of a total of 130,000 engineers.[8]

One of these 41 women was probably Elsie Eaves, a 1920 civil engineering graduate from the University of Colorado, who had just embarked on what would be an illustrious career. Eaves was instrumental in establishing a national organization for women engineers: the Society of Women Engineers and Architects. In 1919, she and several of her colleagues at the University of Colorado wrote to engineering schools across the country, asking for information on women engineering students and graduates. They found 63 women enrolled in engineering at 20 universities—including 43 at the University of Michigan alone! The Michigan women had organized a group of their own, the T-Square Society, in 1914. Most schools, however, did not yet admit women to their engineering programs. One professor responded to Eaves' letter: "I would state that we have not now, have never had, and do not expect to have in the near future, any women students registered in our engineering department."[9] In the end, there were too few women engineers around the country and they were too scattered geographically to keep the organization alive, so it folded.[10]

Women engineers made little headway in the 1920s and 1930s. Despite the economic boom in the 1920s and the accompanying optimism and expansion, women in the professions generally did not benefit from the strong economy. Out of 197 fellowships awarded in engineering during one period of the 1920s, one went to a woman. However, the number of women engineering graduates did grow by 113 from 1920-1929, to a total of 158. And 53 engineering colleges (an increase from 35 in 1920) now admitted women.[11]

Those women who were able to graduate with a degree and find employment still faced significant obstacles in advancing their careers. After graduation, a man would start as a junior engineer and could generally expect, if his performance was satisfactory, to be promoted to senior engineer and then project engineer. Then, he would move on to management, with each step representing increased status, power, and salary. Women engineers, however, were usually limited to desk work, sometimes bordering on clerical work, and did not have access to plant or field work, which denied them the necessary experience to move up the ladder. Many higher level positions required travel to remote locations, behavior not acceptable for "gentle women." Women often needed advanced training—not generally required of men. Although a few women were able to hold positions with professional responsibility, many others operated on the fringes of the profession as writers, editors, secretaries, librarians, industrial teachers, or laboratory assistants—all more acceptable positions than being an actual engineer.[12]

Great Depression

Men and women alike were forced to cope when the stock market crashed in 1929, and the Great Depression followed. Many women had to sacrifice personal ambition and accept a life of economic inactivity.[13] Thus many women engineers either voluntarily or involuntarily ceased their careers after 1929. Jobs in general were scarce, and what jobs were available were unlikely to be given to women.

However, as college enrollments dwindled, colleges began to look for women as students. Twenty-seven more engineering schools began to admit women and the number of female engineering graduates increased by 156 during 1930-1939. With a new emphasis on graduate education for engineers as a result of technology developments during World War I, it is interesting that six schools that excluded women at the undergraduate level allowed them to pursue graduate engineering degrees. Prior to 1942, 18 women had received master's degrees across the entire U.S. One woman did receive an engineering Ph.D. in 1920, but no more women earned that capstone degree again until three women did so in the 1930s. However, women still accounted for only about three out of every 1,000 engineers. And no women were on the engineering faculty at any of the 20 largest doctoral universities in the country in 1938.[14]

By 1938, the percentage of women in engineering represented significantly less than one half of one percent of all engineers. Although it was estimated that about 1,000 women engineers and architects were trained in the U.S., the 1938 edition of *American Men of Science* reported eight women, representing 0.2 percent of its approximately 3,500 engineers.[15] The 1940 census listed 730 women employed as engineers, less than 0.3 percent of the total; but many of those are thought not to have had the education credentials (see Table 3-1). And in 1938, there were zero women engineers among the almost 20,000 engineers employed in the Federal classified civil service.[16]

[17]

Table 3-1						
Distribution by Branch of Engineering of Men and Women Employed as Professional Engineers, 1940						
Branch of engineering	Total	Number		Percent		Percent women are of total
		Men	Women	Men	Women	
All employed professional engineers	245,288	244,558	730	100.0	100.0	0.3
Civil engineers	80,362	80,171	191	32.8	26.2	0.2
Mechanical engineers	82,443	82,255	188	33.6	25.8	0.2
Electrical engineers	53,267	53,103	164	21.7	22.5	0.3
Industrial engineers	9,283	9,209	74	3.8	10.1	0.8
Mining and metallurgical engineers	8,813	8,739	74	3.6	10.1	0.8
Chemical engineers	11,120	11,081	39	4.5	5.3	0.4

The highly visible women described in our profiles either were linked with a male relative who was making a significant impact in the engineering field, or were so outstanding on their own that their accomplishments could not be ignored. Female engineering students were still aliens in a man's world and had to deal with both implicit and explicit constraints in their educations and in their jobs, constraints which often relegated them to the margins of the profession. In addition, the number of women in engineering was so small, that no feminized branches of engineering even had a chance to develop.[18] Most women were still not admitted to the professional engineering societies in their field of expertise, and a nationwide organization for women engineers had not yet been established.

World War II

World War II, similar to World War I, presented opportunities for women to assist in the war effort. This movement of women back into the work force is often personified by famed metalworker and poster woman "Rosie the Riveter." Rosie is portrayed as a powerful woman, pictured in a headscarf while displaying large arm muscles (her sleeves are rolled up), with the caption, "We Can Do It!"[19] Although World War I had seen the serious use of technology for airplanes, submarines, tanks, bombs, and other equipment, technological development and organized scientific research had evolved in the ensuing 20 years such that the machines of World War II were even more destructive and more powerful. Consequently they needed engineers and technicians to design, build, and maintain them. Many of the men with the skills to fill these engineering and technical jobs were now in the military.[20]

Women were encouraged to enter the work force because the men were gone. Indeed, they began to be invited into the good positions, not just those invisible jobs discounted as "women's work."[21] People were needed at drawing boards, in engineering shops to keep planes, tanks, and other essential materials rolling off the assembly line—everywhere that the war effort needed support. The problem for the government was that with the men gone, women and blacks, the two reserve labor forces of the country, were the only ones available to fill these positions. But there were not enough appropriately trained women or blacks. In engineering, the shortages were so great that women were vigorously recruited during World War II.[22]

The Office of War Information (OWI) and the War Manpower Commission began issuing literature and propaganda glorifying women as scientists and engineers to bolster the war effort. In 1942, a film, *Women in Defense*, narrated by Kathryn Hepburn from a script written by Eleanor Roosevelt, urged women to go to work in government or on scientific projects. In 1942, the movie *Madame Curie*, starring award-winning Greer Garson, was released, further glorifying women's contributions in science. New training programs for scientists and engineers were established and, by 1943, women (and to some extent, blacks) were being specially recruited and trained for jobs in industry. Bright high school students were sought out and urged to major in science in college through the Westinghouse National Science Talent Search (established 1943) and the Bausch and Lomb Science Talent Search (established 1944). Both programs had women among their early winners, and the Westinghouse program even required that the percentage of female winners be proportional to female entrants. Books and articles were released during the 1942 through 1945 period urging women to pursue careers in science and engineering. Edna Yost's book *American Women of Science* (1943), which lauded women's past and current contributions to science, and painted a bright picture for women in these fields.[23]

To fill the personnel gap, the U.S. government began running crash courses in science, engineering, and management for both men and women after the war began. Some specific courses were targeted at helping women become engineering aides and engineering cadettes. Many engineering schools set up special engineering training courses for women sponsored by the War Department, the Signal Corps, the Ordinance Department, and the Air Force. Twenty-nine institutions that had heretofore excluded women, including the Carnegie Institute of

Technology, Columbia University's School of Engineering, and Rensselaer Polytechnic Institute, admitted women engineering students for the first time between 1940 and 1945, to train them in support of the war effort.[24]

Engineering Aides, Engineering Cadettes and Engineers

In 1942 and 1943, the call went out for more women engineers. Elsie Eaves (profiled at the end of this chapter), of the *Engineering News-Record*, warned women that the word "engineer" was being applied to to very different career paths: Those few women with degrees in the field that could expect to be hired into professional positions. But those non-engineering college female graduates with a few additional courses in drafting and machine testing, and those women without college degrees, were hired into subprofessional jobs as "engineering aides" or "engineering cadettes." Sometimes, they were temporary assistants to men who had been promoted from lower positions within the organization. Nonetheless, there were plenty of jobs for both kinds of "engineers" at this point. Even the federal government changed its longtime policy and began to hire female engineers in 1942.[25]

The demand was so great for the subordinate type of personnel (those classified as "aides" or "cadettes") that a special program was set up by the federal government as early as October 1940 in anticipation of entering World War II. The U.S. Office of Education administered this "defense training" program that was funded by a special appropriation. It was one of the first federal government efforts to increase and train scientific manpower. Manpower shortages were expected to be severe if the U.S. entered the war—the aircraft industry on Long Island and in New Jersey alone would require about half of all the engineering graduates nationwide. The first Emergency Defense Training (EDT) program course was offered in December 1940, and by June 1941, over 100,000 people (almost all men) had received training in engineering subjects.[26]

At first, the Engineering, Science, and Management War Training program (ESMWT) offered training only at four-year technical schools. Colleges were responsible for determining local training needs and developing courses to meet those needs, but not to provide a complete engineering education nor necessarily any academic credit for the courses.[27] As the war continued and personnel shortages intensified, the program and the corresponding training was extended to a total of 227 colleges and universities, including several women's colleges, where courses were taught in elementary engineering, mathematics, chemistry, physics, and safety engineering. The ESMWT opened doors of opportunity to many women and some minorities.[28] In a report issued in December 1942, the ESMWT reported classes offered at Clarkson, Cornell, the University of Rochester, Syracuse University, Rensselaer Polytechnic Institute, and Union College. Union College had, in fact, given courses to 145 women out of 817 students, including a special course in electricity and mechanics for "girl high school graduates employed on testing work in the Engineering Department of the General Electric Company."[29]

In 1943 and 1944, 21.8 percent of the enrollees were women and minorities. By 1945, over 1.8 million people had been trained, including 280,000 women (15.7 percent) and 25,000 blacks (1.4 percent).[30] About one-fifth of these women were enrolled in engineering drawing, while significant numbers were learning aeronautical engineering, inspection and testing, mapping and surveying, and engineering fundamentals; the rest were registered for other scientific and management courses.[31]

Other departments of the federal government conducted their own programs to recruit and train women for technical positions. The Office of the Chief of Ordnance trained women with high school mathematics for civil service appointments as junior engineering aides during a three-month intensive course at the University of Michigan. Female engineering aides for the Frankford and Picatinny Arsenals were trained at similar programs sponsored at Rutgers University, Drexel Institute, Temple University, and the University of Pennsylvania. The Signal Corps and the Army Air Forces provided technical training to hundreds of women who were often then assigned clerical duties, which resulted in a high turnover rate.[32]

Some companies had other training requirements or couldn't wait for the results of the government programs to bear fruit. General Electric recruited women with degrees in math or physics and then gave them on-the-job training so that they could handle computations in GE's machine-tool department. However, so few women existed with these types of credentials, that the companies began reaching down further, pursuing women still in college.[33]

Aircraft companies started special programs for engineering aides and engineering cadettes. The Goodyear Aircraft Corporation developed a six-month program in aeronautical engineering at the University of Cincinnati to prepare women as "junior engineers."[34]

The Vega Aircraft Corporation needed aircraft design engineers starting in 1941. In cooperation with Lockheed Aircraft Corporation and the California Institute of Technology, their engineering shortage was temporarily solved by hiring engineers trained in other disciplines—civil, mechanical, or electrical—from other industries and training them for aircraft work with eight weeks of college-level instruction at Cal Tech, followed by eight weeks of an on-the-job apprenticeship. Other technical and clerical employees with some experience took evening classes specially arranged with the University of California in aircraft engineering-related subjects. But soon, all available candidates for these programs had been trained.

Next, Vega established a full-time training program at the University of California at Los Angeles (UCLA) to teach drafting for women. These women were not already employees, but were guaranteed jobs if they finished the course.

By 1943, Vega established a full-time 52-week program at Cal Tech for two groups of 20 full-time employees. The 40 students, all women, ranged in age from 18 to 49 years old, and already worked in the engineering department at Vega. They were able to take a full college course in engineering, stripped of all non-essentials, and earn the chance to be upgraded to higher level jobs.[35]

In 1942, the Curtiss-Wright airplane company developed a plan for training "CW Cadettes," young women with at least two years of college education, including one year of college-level mathematics. Seven colleges, some of which had never previously enrolled women—Cornell, Penn State, Purdue, Minnesota, Texas, Rensselaer Polytechnic Institute (RPI), and Iowa State—gave over 600 women a 10-month crash course of engineering, math, job terminology, aircraft drawing, engineering mechanics, airplane materials, theory of flight, and aircraft production. After their training, these cadettes were assigned to airplane plants to work in research, testing, and production.[36]

The Engineering Cadette Program in the School of Electrical Engineering at Purdue University sponsored by Radio Corporation of America (RCA) helped convince skeptical faculty that women could excel technically and academically. Cadettes accounted for 20 percent of the engineering staff in some RCA plants, allowing women to move beyond being tokens.[37]

By 1945, the number of women engineers listed on the National Roster had increased from 144 in 1941 to 395 (an amazing increase of almost 300 percent in four years), mostly at the bachelor's level. And many more engineering colleges and universities now at least had seen women as students.[38] The number of women enrolled as engineering undergraduates had increased to 1,800 by 1945.[39]

Faculty

Women were also encouraged to become faculty members at colleges and universities, temporarily replacing men who had been called into government service or into the military. In fact, a significant number of female scientists, including mathematicians and chemists, who were not working on other war projects, moved into the ranks of college and university faculty. In 1942, 2,412 women scientists (including 50 women in engineering out of a total of 5,394 engineering teachers) were on science faculties. By 1946, the number had increased to 7,746 (an over 200 percent increase in four years) and the number of women engineering faculty, including some women who taught at all-male institutions, had increased to fifty-three.[40]

These women cadettes, engineering aides, engineers in industry, and faculty all made significant contributions to the war effort, and to the advancement and acceptance of women in technical fields. All in all, about 45,000 women were trained for engineering jobs during World War II.[41]

After World War II

When the war ended, millions of veterans—primarily men—came home expecting to be gainfully employed. Many of the women who had been employed found themselves no longer welcome in the work force. In fact, these women were now expected to go home and raise babies or "go back to the kitchen" and not steal work from returning GIs. The recent educational programs were shut down. And because many engineering schools still did not admit women, educational opportunities for women who wanted to pursue an engineering career were once again severely limited. By January 1946, 4 million women had left the labor force.[42]

By the time World War II ended, however, women were not quite as eager to accept the inevitable as they were when World War I ended. They began generating statistics and scientific data to prove they were just as capable as men and were being treated unfairly. Still, even for those who managed to hold on to their positions, they were unable to advance as men did. Women were still channeled into less challenging work, kept in lower ranks, and paid lower salaries by employers who minimized their contributions.[43]

A very significant impact of the war's end was the GI Bill, which provided funds for veterans' education. Schools that had been underutilized during the war were suddenly faced with a deluge of male students. It is estimated that 7.8 million veterans chose to take advantage of the GI

Bill's educational provisions. Female enrollment at some coeducational schools had reached 50 percent or higher during the war, but as the demand for slots increased, many institutions introduced or reintroduced maximum quotas on female enrollment. Some colleges refused to accept applications from out-of-state women. Women were told that space was not available and that they would have to attend other institutions. For a few years, women who were already in the educational pipeline, women veterans and wartime female "engineering aides" getting engineering undergraduate degrees, contributed to a brief expansion in the number of women getting engineering degrees. Through the 1950s, the percentage of women dropped to just 25-35 percent of the total college undergraduate enrollment. The number of women graduating with engineering degrees declined as well.[44]

Discrimination against women was widespread; women were systematically pushed out of science and engineering at the undergraduate level, at the graduate level, and as faculty. Men even took over women's dormitories, and many universities added temporary housing to accommodate the returning male GIs. Male veterans replaced female staff and faculty as well as female engineering students. There were no discrimination laws in place (these would not be enacted until the 1960s or later) to prevent any of this behavior. The nation was also extremely grateful to its veterans and felt there was, in many cases, a duty to make their adjustment to civilian life as easy as possible. Objections or protests were few and far between and not effective. And society as a whole was still quite ambivalent about the proper role for women. These ambitious women in engineering, who were certainly atypical, threatened presumed male and female spheres.[45]

The Outlook for Women in Architecture and Engineering, a Bulletin of the Women's Bureau of the U.S. Department of Labor, printed in 1948, painted a bleak picture for women in engineering:[46]

> Advancement for women in engineering is conceded to be difficult. They seldom follow the usual line from junior engineer to senior engineer to project engineer,

nor are they often transferred to nonengineering work in sales, purchasing or administration. Usually limited by custom to office work, as compared with field or plant work, women engineers rarely find opportunities to obtain the rounded experience necessary for normal progression. The fact that many of the positions representing advancement often require field work or travel to remote locations further reduces their chances. However, a few women have broken through these bounds.

Women engineers, who had been welcomed with open arms during the war years, were now told to abandon the idea of an engineering career. The Women's Bureau, a unit of the Department of Labor, reported that there were 950 women in engineering as of 1946-47. These women constituted only 0.3 percent of the total 317,000 engineers in the U.S. Of course, this was much higher than the eight women reported to be practicing engineering in the 1949 edition of *American Men of Science*, which despite its title, reported on all individuals practicing in the sciences. The U.S. census of 1950 counted 6,475 women employed as engineers, of whom only 41 percent had four years or more of college, and 17 percent had not graduated from high school. Probably about 3,600 of these women were truly engineering professionals. There were now an adequate number of women in engineering to finally constitute enough of a critical mass to move the cause of women in engineering forward, both to seek more women as engineers, and to improve career opportunities for those already in the field.[47]

In fact, women seeking careers or advancement in their existing careers and students studying engineering started to band together for mutual support and job-hunting help. In the late 1940s, the war-support effort and the associated defense industry had made cutbacks across the board. Employment for many engineering disciplines was at a low. Many professional societies still excluded women, either outright or by refusing them full membership, and thus had very few women among their membership (see Table 3-2). But, this time, efforts for mutual support among women engineers were enabled by a nationwide infrastructure that had not existed in 1919. Now there was the telephone, the automobile, the highway, and the railroad.[48] Female engineers fueled by isolation and discrimination, and the national infrastructure, founded the Society of Women Engineers (SWE) in 1949-1950.[49]

Table 3-2 Membership in the Founder Societies, 1946		
Organization	Total Membership	Number of women members
American Institute of Electrical Engineers	24,526	14
American Society of Civil Engineers	21,100	23
American Society of Mechanical Engineers	20,060	33
American Institute of Mining and Metallurgical Engineers	12,600	26
American Institute of Chemical Engineers	5,788	5

50

Society of Women Engineers

The Society of Women Engineers traces its founding back to a group of female students at Drexel University in Philadelphia and a gathering of Cooper Union (an engineering college in New York City) and City College of New York graduates at Green Engineering Camp of the Cooper Union in New Jersey. The Drexel students had begun meeting in 1948, calling themselves the "Philadelphia District of the Society of Women Engineers." The Camp Green meeting, held May 25, 1950, actually resulted in the official founding of SWE. The first president, Beatrice Hicks, was elected, membership requirements were established, and dues were set. Women attending the Camp Green meeting were also from Boston and Washington, D.C., and represented two major constituencies: (1) The pioneers—those who had been trained and were working as engineers prior to or during World War II; and (2), the engineering aides who had returned to college after the war to get their engineering degrees.[51]

The objectives of the organization were:

· To inform the public of the availability of qualified women for engineering positions; to foster a favorable attitude in industry towards women engineers; and to contribute to their professional advancement.

· To encourage young women with suitable aptitudes and interest to enter the engineering profession, and to guide them in their educational programs.

· To encourage membership in other technical and professional engineering societies, participation in their activities, and adherence to their code of ethics.[52]

One of the first orders of business for SWE was the establishment of the Achievement Award. This award, the highest tribute given by SWE, honors a woman engineer of outstanding achievement.[53]

1952: Maria Telkes: "In recognition of her meritorious contributions to the utilization of solar energy."

1953: Elsie Gregory MacGill: "In recognition of her meritorious contributions to aeronautical engineering."

1954: Edith Clarke: "In recognition of her many original contributions to stability theory and circuit analysis."

1955: Margaret H. Hutchinson: "In recognition of her significant contributions to the field of chemical engineering."

1956: E'lise F. Harmon: "In recognition of her significant contributions to the area of component and circuit miniaturization."

1957: Rebecca H. Sparling: "In recognition of her meritorious contributions to high temperature metallurgy and non-destructive testing of metals."

The organization grew rapidly, numbering 350 in 1953 and surpassing 500 by 1958. The group received decent publicity too—early activities of SWE were reported in *The New York Times*.[54]

Finally, there was an organization willing to accept women engineers, recognize them for their accomplishments, and encourage other women to be engineers.

KEY WOMEN OF THIS PERIOD

Mary Engle Pennington (1872 – 1952)

Mary Engle Pennington was the first woman member of the American Society of Refrigerating Engineers. Her picture hangs today at its successor organization—the American Society of Heating, Refrigerating and Air-Conditioning Engineers. She later became the president of the American Institute of Refrigeration. In 1947, she was elected a fellow of the American Society of Refrigerating Engineers and a fellow of the American Association for the Advancement of Science (AAAS).

Pennington completed the coursework for a bachelor's degree in chemistry, biology, and hygiene at the University of Pennsylvania, but at that time (1892), the University did not grant bachelor's degrees to women. Instead, she received a Certificate of Proficiency in biology. She continued her studies and in 1895, received a Ph.D. in chemistry from the University of Pennsylvania.

Her work in refrigeration led to her appointment as head of the Department of Agriculture's food research laboratory. As she used the name "M.E. Pennington," not everyone was aware that she was a woman. In 1916, when she had been chief of the Food Research Laboratory for a decade, a railroad vice-president on whom she called, instructed his secretary "to get rid of the woman," because he had "an appointment with Dr. Pennington, the government expert."

Pennington developed standards of milk and dairy inspection that were adopted by health boards throughout the country. Her methods of preventing spoilage of eggs, poultry, and fish were adopted by the food warehousing, packaging, transportation, and distribution industries. She has six patents associated with refrigeration and spoilage prevention methods. The standards she established for refrigerated railroad cars, which she developed by riding freight trains, remained in effect for many years and gained her worldwide recognition as a perishable food expert. Pennington received the Garvan Medal from the American Chemical Society in 1940, and was the first woman elected to the American Poultry Historical Society's Hall of Fame (1947).[55]

Lillian Moller Gilbreth (1878 – 1972)

Lillian Moller Gilbreth, fondly referred to as the "first lady of engineering," is best known to the general population as the mother of twelve on whom the book and movie *Cheaper by the Dozen* was based. She was a pioneer in recognizing the interrelationship between engineering and human relations. Her work in industrial engineering and time and motion studies helped encourage the development of industrial engineering curricula in engineering schools. With her husband, Frank Gilbreth, who was a pioneer in scientific management and a determined researcher, Lillian Gilbreth showed companies how to improve management techniques, and how to increase industrial efficiency and production by budgeting time and energy, as well as money. Her work eventually led to career suitability tests, fatigue elimination studies, and the idea of skill transfer from one job to another (the "psychology of management").

The Gilbreths worked together in many areas. They provided scientific management consulting through their firm (Gilbreth, Inc.) that advised many companies. They wrote and researched together and authored hundreds of documents. They lectured at companies, universities, and professional societies. They conducted the Gilbreth summer schools on management topics. And, of course, they raised 12 children. Lillian Gilbreth, however, continued to work in the field for decades after

Frank's untimely death in 1924, and accomplished much in the field of industrial engineering alone.

Gilbreth joined the faculty at Purdue University in 1935 as a full professor of management after having served as a lecturer and advisor for a number of years. She continued to serve as an academic advisor to female students from 1948 until shortly before her death in 1972. She became head of the Department of Personnel Relations at Newark College of Engineering in 1941, and visiting professor of management at the University of Wisconsin at Madison in 1955.

In 1921, Gilbreth was named an honorary member of the Society of Industrial Engineers at a point when they still did not admit women to membership. In 1966, she was the first woman to receive the Hoover Medal for distinguished public service by an engineer. SWE named her its first honorary member in 1950 (her membership number was one) and she was one of the organization's staunchest supporters for the rest of her life. SWE established its first scholarship in 1958 and named it the Lillian Moller Gilbreth Scholarship. In 1965, she became the first woman elected to the National Academy of Engineering. The recipient of 23 honorary degrees, Gilbreth was also the recipient of the first awarding of the Gilbreth Medal from the Society of Industrial Engineers in 1931. Gilbreth was the first engineer honored by a stamp in the Great American series of stamps by the U.S. Postal Service in 1984. Gilbreth was inducted into the National Women's Hall of Fame in 1995.[56]

Edith Clarke (1883-1959)

Edith Clarke had always wanted to be an engineer. However, in 1908, when she graduated from Vassar, engineering was not offered nor encouraged for women. Thus, she began three years of work as a teacher, then enrolled at the University of Wisconsin where she studied civil engineering for a year. She then was employed by American Telephone and Telegraph (AT&T) in New York City, where she supervised women who did computations for research engineers. Finally, she enrolled at the Massachusetts Institute of Technology (MIT) in electrical engineering and received her master's degree in 1919, the first woman awarded such a degree from MIT. After graduation, she had a very difficult time securing employment as an electrical engineer. Although she wanted to work at either Westinghouse Electric or General Electric, neither company had an opening for a woman engineer. Finally, in 1920, General Electric offered Clarke a job directing calculations in the turbine engine department, a job very similar to the one she had had at AT&T.

However, since she wasn't being allowed to do electrical engineering work, she left GE to be an instructor at the Constantinople Women's College in Turkey. Finally, when she returned from Turkey in 1922, GE offered her a job as an electrical engineer in the central station engineering department. At GE, she became extremely interested in the system of symmetrical components, which is a mathematical means for engineers to study and solve problems of power system losses and performance of electrical equipment. Clarke was the first woman to address the American Institute of Electrical Engineers, which she did in 1926 on the topic of "Steady-State Stability in Transmission Systems." She adopted this system to three-phase components (the basis of our electricity in the United States). Clarke then wrote a textbook, *Circuit Analysis of AC Power Systems, Symmetrical and Related Components* (1943), and a second volume in 1950, that was used to educate all power system engineers for many years. Based on these significant contributions, Clarke was one of the first three women fellows of AIEE.

Clarke left General Electric to become a professor of electrical engineering at the University of Texas. While there, she attracted much publicity as she was the first woman professor of electrical engineering to teach at a university in the U.S. Clarke received the SWE Achievement Award in 1954 for "her many original contributions to stability theory and circuit analysis."[57]

Olive Dennis (1885-1957)

Olive Dennis first studied mathematics and science at Goucher College. After several years as a teacher, she completed a degree in civil engineering from Cornell (1920), with a specialization in structural engineering. That fall, she went to work in the bridge department of the Baltimore and Ohio Railroad. However, the president of the B&O railroad had other ideas about how she could contribute to the organization. After 14 months in the bridge department, Dennis was promoted to the position of Engineer of Service for the railroad, riding the rails and figuring out ways to make the railroad more accommodating to its passengers.

During her years with the railroad, Dennis pushed for better lighting and better seating (cleaner, better fabrics, and lower, reclining seats) in the coach cars. She was an advocate for air conditioning in the cars and she designed and received a patent for an individually-operated ventilator. Dennis even designed and patented the blue colonial china provided in the dining car. At the Women's Centennial Congress in New York in 1940, she was named by Carrie Chapman Catt as one of the 100 outstanding career women in the United States.[58]

Elsie Eaves (1898-1983)

Elsie Eaves was elected a Fellow member of the SWE in 1980, the first year SWE elected Fellows. At that time it was said that Eaves "always encouraged women by her active example and participation." A life member of SWE, she served on the SWE Board of Trustees and had numerous firsts to her credit. She graduated from the University of Colorado at Boulder in 1920 with a B.S. in civil engineering (with honors). In her first jobs, she was a draftsman for the U.S. Bureau of Reclamation, Denver & Rio Grande Railroad, and the Colorado State Highway Department; an instructor of engineering mathematics at her alma mater; and an office engineer for Colonel Herbert S. Crocker, consulting engineer, and for Crocker & Fischer, contractors in Denver, Colorado.

Then she headed to New York City and began employment with McGraw-Hill, the publishing company. The late Col. Willard T. Chevalier hired Eaves (after an editor of an undisclosed organization told her "a woman's place, if not in the home, is in the department store") and created her job as assistant on market surveys for *Engineering News-Record* in 1926. She became Director of Market Surveys for *Engineering News-Record* and *Construction Methods and Equipment* shortly thereafter. In 1932, Eaves moved to the position of Manager of Business News Department, where she directed the activities of 100 staffers throughout the U.S. and Canada.

Her career in the publishing field was a series of "firsts." In 1929, Eaves originated and compiled the first national inventory of municipal and industrial sewage disposal facilities—an analysis that she recompiled at regular intervals. A few years later, she compiled statistics on needed construction, which aided the passage of the Federal Loan-Grant legislation used to revitalize the construction industry during the 1931-1935 depression. In 1945, she organized and directed the *Engineering News-Record's* measurement of Post War Planning by the Construction Industry that was used by the Committee for Economic Development and the American Society of Civil Engineers as the official progress report of the industry. This index was unprecedented in the field of engineering analysis. Under Eaves's direction, the "Post War Planning" statistics were converted into a continuous inventory of planned construction. This has become the *Engineering News-Record's* "Backlog of Proposed Construction," an index to more than $100 billion of construction activity. Another of her unique "firsts" was defining the limits and editing the pilot issues of the *Construction Daily*, a nationwide service.

Eaves's list of firsts and awards are extensive:

- First woman to be licensed as a professional engineer in New York State
- First woman member of the American Society of Civil Engineers (ASCE) (as a corporate member in 1927).
- First woman to be a life member of the ASCE (1962, at which time there were 54 women among 48,000 members).
- First woman elected to honorary membership of the ASCE (1979); first woman to be elected Associate Member, Fellow of ASCE.

- First and, for a long time, the only woman member of the American Association of Cost Engineers (1957) as well as the first civil engineer.
- First woman to receive the Honorary Life Membership Award from the American Association of Cost Engineers (1973).
- First woman to receive the International Executive Service Corporation "Service to the Country" award.
- First woman to receive the American Association of Cost Engineer's Award of Merit (1967).[59]

Elsie MacGill (1905-1980)

Elsie MacGill was stricken by polio while she was studying for her master's degree in aeronautical engineering at the University of Michigan. She wrote her examinations from the hospital and received her degree in 1929. This was after her successful receipt of a bachelor's degree in electrical engineering at the University of Toronto (1927). For both of her degrees, she was the first woman to receive a degree in that field at that University. After her convalescence, she worked on her doctorate degree for two years at MIT.

Subsequent to earning her Ph.D., she joined the Fairchild Aircraft Company as an airplane designer and performed experiments in stress analysis. Later, she served as chief aeronautical engineer for the Canadian Car and Foundry Company. One of her major projects there was to build Hurricane Fighter Planes for the British Air Ministry. These planes had precise requirements for many of each plane's 25,000 parts to allow them to be interchangeable between planes. MacGill was responsible for transforming a railway boxcar manufacturer into an aircraft factory to complete this job. Later, she engineered production of the Curtiss Helldiver for the U.S. Navy.

MacGill received the SWE Achievement Award in 1953 "in recognition of her meritorious contributions to aeronautical engineering." She was also recognized for her accomplishments in Canada, where she was the first woman member of the Engineering Institute of Canada and the first woman to read a paper before it. She later became the first woman to serve as a technical advisor to the U.N.'s International Civil Aviation Organization, where she helped draft international air-worthiness regulations for commercial aircraft. She was inducted posthumously into Canada's Aviation Hall of Fame and is profiled in the Canadian Science and Engineering Hall of Fame.

MacGill was also an outspoken advocate of equal pay for equal work before the concept became popular. In 1967, she became a member of the Royal Commission on the Status of Women in Canada.[60]

Beatrice Hicks (1919 – 1979)

One of the founders of the Society of Women Engineers, Beatrice Hicks served as its first president. She was committed to the organization because of her belief that there was a great future for women in engineering. Because of her interest in mathematics, physics, chemistry and mechanical drawing in high school, she decided to become an engineer. In fact, her interest had been sparked at age 13 when her engineer father had taken her to see the Empire State Building and the George Washington Bridge, and she had learned that it was engineers who built such structures. Her parents didn't actively discourage her, although her high school classmates and some of her teachers tried to discourage her, pointing out that engineering was not a proper field for women.

After her high school graduation in 1935, she entered the Newark (New Jersey) College of Engineering. Since it was during the depression, she needed to earn money for her expenses. In 1939, she received a B.S. in chemical engineering and took a position as a research assistant at the College. In 1942, she got a job with the Western Electric Company, becoming the first woman to be employed by the firm as an engineer. She worked first in the test set design department and later in the quartz crystal department. An early award citation stated "the quality of her work became legend." She studied at night while employed and, in 1949, earned an M.S. in physics from Stevens Institute. Subsequently, she undertook further graduate work at Columbia University.

When her father died in 1946, she became vice-president and chief engineer of the company he had founded, Newark Controls Company, a firm specializing in environmental sensing devices. In 1955, she bought control of the company and became president. One of the major products of the company at that time was low-water cutoffs and other devices to protect people from their own forgetfulness, often sold through mail-order companies. Here, Hicks was also involved in the design, development, and manufacture of pressure- and gas-density controls for aircraft and missiles. In 1959, she was awarded patent 3,046,369 for a molecular density scanner or gas density switch. This type of switch is a key component in systems using artificial atmospheres. After 1967, when her husband died, she became the owner of his firm, Rodney D. Chipp & Associates, a consulting firm.

In 1952, she was named "Women of the Year" in industry by *Mademoiselle* magazine. In 1961, she was the first woman engineer appointed by the U.S. Secretary of Defense to the Defense Advisory Committee on Women in the Sciences. Hicks received SWE's Achievement Award in 1963 "in recognition of her significant contributions to the theoretical study and analysis of sensing devices under extreme environmental conditions, and her substantial achievements in international technical understanding, professional guidance, and engineering education." She was the first woman to receive an honorary doctorate from Rensselear Polytechnic Institute (1965). She also received an honorary Sc.D. from Hobart and William Smith Colleges and from the Stevens Institute of Technology (both in 1978). In 1978, she was elected to the National Academy of Engineering, the sixth woman to be elected. In 2001, she was inducted posthumously to the National Women's Hall of Fame.[61]

Chapter Four
SUBURBIA AND SPUTNIK

The Korean War

With the start of the Cold War, and then the Korean War in 1950, American women were once again asked to contribute to the nation's defense. Young women were even *encouraged* to study science and engineering. In 1951, President Harry Truman was seeking a standing army of 3.5 million men and highly trained human resources at home—scientists and engineers, not only for Korea, but anywhere necessary for the foreseeable future. The shortage of these resources was especially acute because of low birth rates during the 1930s and a drop in engineering enrollments after World War II because of highly publicized unemployment in engineering in 1949 and 1950.[1]

A need for technical manpower was growing out of the increasingly complex machines and processes used by society. A 1951 report describing the differences between a B-47 jet bomber and earlier models demonstrates the higher levels of complexity.[2]

> The B-47 jet bomber, now entering volume production,
> required two years for design, two more years to reach
> test flight stage, and two more years to start assembly

line production. A B-47 is made up of some 72,000 parts exclusive of nuts, bolts, and rivets. The B-47 requires 40 miles of wiring compared to 10 miles for the B-29. A B-47 contains over 1,500 electronic tubes. The wing skin must be tapered in thickness throughout its entire length, from five-eighths inch at the body joint to three-sixteenths inch at the wing tip. The first B-47 plane required 3,464,000 engineering man-hours compared to 85,000 man-hours for the first production model of the B-17.

A 1951 survey by the National Society of Professional Engineers reported that 65 percent of employers canvassed would hire women engineers if they were available, 45 percent had found it feasible to use them, and 23 percent actually employed women at that time. Although women were being sought as engineers again—at least by some employers—the women engineers in the work force were paid less than men, and their advancement was restricted, often by official company policy.[3]

The Office of Defense Mobilization, in its Defense Manpower Policy No. 8 (September 1952), published a statement advocated by Arthur Flemming, assistant to the director for manpower of ODM and a strong supporter of women. The statement read: "Throughout this document all references to scientists and engineers make no distinction between the sexes or between racial groups; it being understood that equality of opportunity to make maximum effective use of intellect and ability is a basic concept of democracy." In addition, the policy's eleventh of 12 recommendations was for employers of scientists and engineers "to reexamine their personnel policies and effect any changes necessary to assure full utilization of women and members of minority groups having scientific and engineering training." Flemming was expressing what was increasingly becoming the official view that women were needed as scientists and engineers. However, full and equal opportunity for women in the engineering field had yet to be realized as the Committee of Specialized Personnel from ODM reported on December 9, 1953:[4]

For the most part, the female graduate [i.e., in engineering and the sciences] has been held down as far as advance in classification and remuneration is concerned. Such action on the part of management is totally unrealistic, and in order to promote the development of our high potential of female scientists and engineers, this unrealistic sex barrier must be broken.

The federal government's official policy throughout the 1950s was to encourage women to enter scientific and technical fields and to urge employers to hire them and utilize them fully (including the federal government itself). However, no federal incentives, such as tax credits for fuller utilization of womanpower or enforcement mechanisms were put in place.[5]

The pendulum had swung again toward encouraging women to be engineers and scientists. The country needed women to be in the work force supporting the war effort when the country is at war, but then expected them to be compliant about being discarded and replaced when the national crisis passed. After the middle of the twentieth century, with higher levels of education and training among women and the general population, such treatment began to prove unacceptable for women. But it would still be several decades before significant progress was made toward even a semblance of equal opportunity for scientific and engineering women.

Off to Suburbia

In spite of official government encouragement during the period of the Korean war and, as noted above, through the early 1950s, the number of women enrolling in college and in engineering programs fell. Women constituted less than 0.5 percent of the total engineering student population, and a large number of colleges and universities did not admit women as students. Indeed, during a typical year in the 1950s, women might earn 100 bachelor's degrees in engineering, and the number of engineering Ph.D's they would earn could be counted on one finger.[6] However, there was some good news for women wishing to pursue an engineering degree. The Georgia Institute of Technology accepted women starting in 1953, and Clemson University opened its doors to women in 1955.[7]

The dwindling numbers reflected low societal tolerance for pioneering women, who were now categorized as deviant.[8] Traditional attitudes were very slow to change. Not atypical were the comments about women in a 1952 article from the *Journal of Engineering Education*:[9]

> Women have certain inherent characteristics which stand them in good stead. For instance, they are conscientious, they know how to use their hands, they are careful about detail, and quite important, they are not adverse to trying something new. Witness, for example, their proclivity to change the furniture around in the house about every three days to see if they can find a more efficient arrangement. This is exactly the procedure that our research scientists use; that is, if you don't know if something will work or not, try it and see. Quite often in scientific studies the going gets pretty rough and girls, being more sensitive and nervous than boys, sometimes become emotionally disturbed by overwork and the fear of failure. These troubles, for the most part, can be solved by the strategic use of a few kind words and a little human understanding. Girls will work their hearts out for you if you handle them right, which usually requires nothing more than a sincere interest in their welfare.

Women in the U.S. in the 1950s were being pulled in two directions at the same time. The average age of marriage for American women dropped to its lowest level during the period 1945-1960. The birth rate soared, especially among the college educated (the children born in this period were called baby boomers). Marriage took precedence over careers. In addition, a mass white exodus to suburbia began and, for the first time, college-educated, middle class women had as many children as poor women did.[10] Television and advertising glorified domesticity and the housewife, especially her role as a consumer. Yet in the increasingly consumer-based economy, more workers were required to design and produce all of the new products. Thus, there were many more economic opportunities for women in the work force.[11]

In the face of declining female enrollments in science and engineering and with the projected shortages of technical manpower, in April 1956, President Eisenhower, with the urging of the Office of Defense Mobilization Director Arthur Flemming, established a National (later called President's) Committee on the Development of Scientists and Engineers (PSCE) to serve as a clearinghouse for the many nongovernmental efforts being undertaken around the country to train more scientists and engineers. Interestingly, 19 men and no women were appointed to this committee, and its vice chairman seemed particularly uninterested in recruiting women into engineering. Not much progress was made on the subject of women in science and engineering up to the point that the committee was disbanded in December 1958. However, the vice chairman's request for a breakdown of engineering data into gender would prove beneficial later for female members of the National Science Foundation's (NSF) Divisional Committee for Scientific Personnel and Education.[12]

Sputnik is Launched

With the launching of Sputnik in October 1957, Americans began to focus their anti-Communist sentiment on science and education. Scientists had begun trying to increase funding and emphasize scientific education earlier in the 1950s as the Cold War intensified. When Sputnik went up, Soviet superiority in science was made quite visible to the

American public. And there was a new tone of urgency in the talk about recruiting women scientists and engineers.[13]

In response, President Eisenhower exhorted the American people to meet the need for thousands of new scientists, saying "this [national security] is for the American people the most critical problem of all...we need scientists by the thousands more than we are now presently planning to have." Further, the President requested that the NSF "develop a program for collection of needed supply, demand, employment and compensation data with respect to scientists and engineers."[14]

NSF accomplished this through its Scientific Manpower Program and its two elements, Manpower Studies and the National Register. This National Register of Scientific and Technical Personnel grew out of the National Roster of World War II and subsequent efforts aimed at Cold War preparedness. The National Register had already begun to collect data in 1954 but published little prior to 1959 when in response to the Sputnik launch, Congress increased the NSF's budget. Consequently much of the data available have significant gaps, and data on women scientists and engineers is particularly incomplete.[15]

The NSF designed programs to provide federal assistance to the "best and brightest" in order to produce the scientists needed for the future and to gather the necessary data. As Congress discussed science budgets and fellowship programs as part of the U.S. response to the Sputnik launch (training scientists and engineers was now a matter of national survival), an article titled "Science Talent Hunt Faces Stiff Obstacle: 'Feminine Fallout'; Officials Fear Many Federal Scholarships Will Go to Girls—Who'll Shun Careers" appeared in as prestigious a newspaper as *The Wall Street Journal*. Because up to one-third of these fellowships were expected to go to women who would marry, have children, and interrupt their careers, the author commented:

> Hence it's inevitable that some Government money will
> go to train scientists who experiment only with different
> household detergents and mathematicians who confine
> their work to adding up grocery bills.

But the author further lamented that it would not be feasible to place quotas on the number of fellowships given to women as this "probably would embroil the Government in a great controversy with the many 'equal rights' advocates among the ladies."[16]

The National Defense Education Act (NDEA) was finally passed by Congress in 1958. The act clearly linked higher education to national defense by declaring:

> The Congress hereby finds and declares that the security of the Nation requires the fullest development of the mental resources and technical skills of its young men and women...

> We must increase our efforts to identify and educate more of the talent of our nation. This requires programs that will give assurance that no student of ability will be denied an opportunity for higher education because of financial need; will correct as rapidly as possible the existing imbalances in our educational programs which have led to an insufficient proportion of our population educated in science, mathematics, and modern foreign languages and trained in technology.

Ten new programs were established upon enactment of the NDEA, including a federal student loan program and a new graduate fellowship program larger and broader than the one at the NSF. These fellowships would continue until 1973.[17]

However, women were still feeling a conflict between their domestic obligations and pursuing a scientific or engineering career. And now with a perceived patriotic duty—especially at a time when recruitment literature stressed that Russian women constituted about half of the combined scientific and engineering work force in that country and 25 percent of the Soviet Union's engineers—articles on both sides of the issue appeared in popular magazines with such titles as "Woman's Place Is in the Lab, too," "Science for the Masses," "Bright Girls: What Place in Society?" "Plight of the Intellectual Girl," and "Female-Ism: New and Insidious."[18]

The first comprehensive study describing U.S. scientific and technical manpower was published in 1964—it did not examine traits such as sex and ethnicity.[19] The NSF also funded a number of studies to identify the factors associated with the low numbers of women in science and engineering. These studies showed that myths about women not being suited for engineering due to ability, emotion, or motivation were just that—myths—and the studies recommended actions to encourage women to pursue engineering.[20]

Post-Sputnik, the major cultural and legislative changes of the 1960s would set the stage for greater numbers of women engineers by the turn of the century.

1960s Activism

The women's movement experienced a dramatic rebirth in the 1960s that later translated into significantly increased professional opportunities for women. That it occurred at the same time as the civil rights movement is probably much less of a coincidence than it appears. The birth of feminism and suffrage in the 1800s had been closely aligned with the abolitionist cause. Now, the rebirth of the women's movement was closely related to the struggle for racial equality. Indeed, the militancy of college students during the 1960s mirrored some of the rebellious activism that had been effective and prominent during the suffrage movement. In the 1960s, protests were held on campuses and in the streets, and students traveled to the South on behalf of civil rights.[21]

Betty Friedan's *Feminine Mystique*, published in 1963, launched an attack on suburban America and the status and roles assigned to women. Friedan meant her book as a call to action, and indeed, many women strengthened their resolve to take charge of their own lives as a result of its publication. Indeed, the percentage of college-educated females who worked outside the home increased from seven percent in 1950 to 25 percent in 1960, as a constant diet of domesticity appeared to not be very attractive or satisfying.[22]

In the 1960s, corrective legislation that addressed women's historically lower status in society relative to men began to roll out, one after the other. And by 1962, 53 percent of all female college graduates were employed, while 36 percent of those with high school diplomas held jobs. Seventy percent of all females who had five or more years of higher education worked.[23]

Presidential Commission on the Status of Women

The Presidential Commission on the Status of Women was convened in 1961 to investigate and suggest remedies for "prejudices and outmoded customs [that] act as barriers to the full realization of women's basic rights." Seven committees representing various facets of American life— civil and political rights, education, federal employment, private employment, home and community, social security and taxes, and protective labor legislation—were involved in the commission's work. Their final report, issued in 1963, proved that in almost every area, women were second-class citizens (remember the Federal government would not even hire women engineers until 1942). President Kennedy took two actions as a result of the work that went into the commission's report:

1. Women were to be on an equal basis with men for Civil Service promotion
2. All executive department promotions were to be based on merit.[24]

Equal Pay Act

After the publication of the report from the commission, and in large part because of its findings, President Kennedy signed the Equal Pay Act, which states that "...no employer shall discriminate between employees on the basis of sex by paying wages for equal work, the performance of which requires equal skill, effort and responsibility, and which are performed under similar working conditions." The act was sponsored by Edith Green of Oregon, one of the most influential members of Congress. It was the first major piece of legislation addressing sexual inequality since the Nineteenth Amendment. Although there were significant exemptions included as part of the Act, the legislation was an important step forward.[25]

Civil Rights Act—Title VII

In 1964, a second major piece of legislation—Title VII of the Civil Rights Act—was passed to prohibit discrimination in employment on the basis of race, religion, color, national origin, and sex. The original intent of the bill was to deal with racial inequality. The amendment adding the word "sex" was proposed by the powerful chair of the House Rules Committee, Howard Smith of Virginia, in an effort to retard its passage. Smith urged Congress "to protect our spinster friends in their 'right' to a husband and family," a conniving plea that was met with roars of laughter. His apparent intent was to burden the entire law with the addition of gender and cause its defeat due to the expected ensuing controversy and ridicule. His strategy of adding sex to the legislation was thought of as a joke. Nonetheless, the amendment to the language was retained, and the law passed. The Equal Employment Opportunity Commission was formed to enforce Title VII and found that most of its complaints were from women, not from minorities as had been expected.[26]

The Dawn of Affirmative Action

In September 1965, President Johnson essentially began affirmative action by signing Executive Order 11246. This order required all companies wishing to do business with the federal government to not only provide equal opportunity for all, but also to take affirmative action (defined as extra steps) to bring their hiring in line with available labor pools by race.[27]

Recognition of Sex Discrimination

Two years later, in 1967, President Johnson signed Executive Order 11375 extending Executive Order 11246 to include "sex" as a protected category. This executive order now required that affirmative action be taken on behalf of women (in addition to minorities, as required by Executive Order 11246) so that hiring was in line with gender proportions as well as racial proportions in the relevant labor pools.[28]

National Organization for Women

In 1966, the National Organization for Women was founded. NOW describes itself as a civil rights organization to bring women into "truly equal partnership with men in all areas of American society." The NOW 1968 Bill of Rights called for support of a wide array of issues including equal and unsegregated education and equal job-training opportunities.[29]

By the end of the 1960s, the U.S. had successfully landed men on the moon, symbolizing American technical and scientific superiority over the Soviet Union. The women's rights and civil rights movements encouraged women and minorities to pursue all career fields—including nontraditional ones such as engineering, although the number of women engineering Ph.D.s in 1968 totaled five nationwide (.02 percent of the total). However by the early to mid-1970s, the Vietnam War, the energy crisis, and a widening awareness of environmental issues somewhat soured Americans on science and technology. Now scientists were needed to help save America from themselves—so maybe women and minorities, with different ways of solving problems—could help.[30]

1970s Progress

The 1970s represented watershed years in the progress of women in engineering and women in the work force, in general. In undergraduate engineering, the one percent barrier was broken—in 1972, 525 women received B.S. degrees, a stunning 1.2 percent of the total degrees. By 1979, the percentage of women receiving undergraduate degrees had increased to nine percent of the total, master's degrees in engineering were up to 5.6 percent, and Ph.D. degrees amounted to 2.2 percent of the total.[31]

Significant legislative advances during the decade included the 1972 passage of the Educational Amendments Act (particularly Title IX), the Equal Employment Opportunity Act of 1972, and the 1972 expansion of the Equal Pay Act. All served to put the public on notice that women were to be treated equally, and either intentionally or inadvertently, all served to open more professional opportunities for women, including engineering opportunities.

Education Amendments Act

Title IX of the Educational Amendments Act prohibited discrimination on the basis of sex in all federally-assisted educational programs. Title IX stated in part, "No person in the United States shall, on the basis of sex, be excluded from participation in, be denied the benefits of, or be subjected to discrimination under any education program or activity receiving federal financial assistance."

Title IX extended the Equal Pay Act and Title VII to educational workers and applied to admissions of females to all public undergraduate institutions, professional schools, graduate schools, and vocational schools. A very significant consequence of this act was that caps on the numbers of women students accepted into medical, law, business, and other professional schools were finally abolished.[32]

Certainly women still weren't at parity with men in employment or education by the end of the 1970s, yet more progress had been made for women pursuing an engineering career in this decade than in any previous decade.

KEY WOMEN OF THIS PERIOD

Maria Telkes (1900-1995)

Hungarian-born Maria Telkes came to the United States in 1925 after earning a Ph.D. in physical chemistry at the University of Budapest. She worked first for the Cleveland Clinic Biophysical Laboratory. She was motivated to find alternatives to coal-fired generation for electricity production because of her horror over coal mine disasters.

When the Massachusetts Institute of Technology (MIT) received a grant from oil magnate Godfrey L. Cabot to conduct research in solar energy conversion, Telkes was appointed a research associate by MIT (1940) to start the development of semiconductors for solar thermoelectric generators. She developed solar distillers to convert sea water into drinking water for use on life rafts. She produced inflatable floating solar stills, weighing one pound and producing twice their weight in drinking water directly from sea water. To store solar heat for a test structure that MIT was developing, Telkes developed the use of heat of fusion of inexpensive salt hydrates that required only one-twentieth of the volume of a water tank. The phase change materials (PCM) were new in this type of application.

As a result of this work, Telkes built the first solar-heated home in 1949 in Dover, Massachusetts. She then participated in the construction of solar heated houses by the Curtiss Wright Company in Princeton, New Jersey, and at the University of Delaware from 1972 to 1977. Later, she applied heat storage principles to storing cold for air conditioning and the use of off-peak electricity for heating and cooling of buildings. Her original chemical heat storage invention at MIT grew into an entirely new technology. She holds 21 patents.

During her career of over 50 years, Telkes was involved in photovoltaics, solar cooking, solar space and water heating, solar distillation, and thermoelectricity. Telkes received the first Society of Women Engineers' (SWE) Achievement Award in 1952 "in recognition of her meritorious contributions to the utilization of solar energy." Dr. Telkes, who was referred to as the "Sun Queen," invented simple solar cookers and ovens during the 1950s and 1960s that will roast, broil, and bake food without using wood, fossil fuels, or animal dung. In 1954, the Ford Foundation granted her $45,000 to develop her solar cooker. Some of her solar energy inventions can also be used for crop drying.[33]

Grace Murray Hopper (1906-1992)

Admiral Grace Murray Hopper was famous for carrying "nanoseconds" around with her. These lengths of wire represented the distance light traveled in a nanosecond (one billionth of a second). She was renowned for trying to convey scientific and engineering terms clearly and coherently to non-technical people.

Hopper, also known as "Amazing Grace" and "The Grandmother of the Computer Age," helped develop languages for computers and developed the first computer compiler—software that translates English (or any other language) into the 0's and 1's that computers understand (machine language). Actually, her first compiler translated English, French, and German into machine language, but the Navy told her to stick with

English because computers didn't understand French and German! Computers truly only understand numbers, but humans can translate those numbers now into English, French, German and even Chinese and Japanese. She was also part of the group that found the first computer "bug"—a moth that had gotten trapped in a relay in the central processor (September 9, 1947). When the boss asked why they weren't making any numbers, they responded that they were "debugging" the computer. Although Admiral Hopper loved to lay claim to the discovery of this first computer "bug" (and it is in the Smithsonian's National Museum of American History), the term bug actually had been in use for many years.

Hopper received the SWE Achievement Award in 1964 "in recognition of her significant contributions to the burgeoning computer industry as an engineering manager and originator of automatic programming systems." She was the first woman to attain the rank of Rear Admiral in the U.S. Navy. The destroyer "Hopper" was commissioned by the U.S. Navy in 1997. Hopper received the National Medal of Technology from President Bush in 1991, the first individual woman to receive the medal: "For her pioneering accomplishments in the development of computer programming languages that simplified computer technology and opened the door to a significantly larger universe of users." She was inducted into the National Women's Hall of Fame in 1994. Hopper said she believed it was always easier to ask for forgiveness than permission. "If you ask me what accomplishment I'm most proud of, the answer would be all of the young people I've trained over the years; that's more important than writing the first compiler."[34]

Yvonne Brill (1924 -)

Aerospace consultant Yvonne Brill works tirelessly to nominate women for awards and to boards, and has served as a role model for several generations of women engineers, including her daughter. Her patented hydrazine/hydrazine resistoject propulsion system (3,807,657—granted April 30, 1974) provided integrated propulsion capability for geostationary satellites and became the standard in the communication satellite industry.

Brill's career began in 1945. She left work to raise three children and then returned to work in her forties. In her outstanding career, she has effectively expanded space horizons. Throughout most of that career, she has been the sole technical woman working on propulsion systems. Her other significant technical achievements include work on propellant management feed systems, electric propulsion, and an innovative propulsion system for the Atmosphere Explorer which, in 1973, allowed scientists to gather extensive data of the earth's thermosphere for the first time. She also managed the development, production, and testing of the Teflon solid propellant pulsed plasma propulsion system aboard the NOVA I spacecraft launched in May 1981.

Brill has been a member of the National Academy of Engineering since 1987 and is a Fellow of SWE and the American Institute of Aeronautics and Astronautics. Among her many awards are the 1986 SWE Achievement Award "for important contributions in advanced auxiliary propulsion of spacecraft and devoted service to the growing professionalism of women in engineering," the 1993 SWE Resnik Challenger Medal for expanding space horizons through innovations in rocket propulsion systems, and induction into the Women in Technology International Hall of Fame in 1999.[35]

Thelma Estrin (1924 -)

Pursuing her electrical engineering education at the University of Wisconsin in the 1940s and 1950s (B.S. 1948, M.S. 1949) was not easy for Thelma Estrin. Her professors did not take her seriously and because she could not get a research assistant position, her Ph.D. (1951) took a year longer than did her husband's.

Then she had to commute for four hours a day to her job in New York City from her home in Princeton, New Jersey because no other opportunities were available. Nevertheless, she persevered, with the support of her husband. They had three daughters in the 1950s.

Estrin was a pioneer in the field of biomedical engineering. She was one of the first to use computer technology to solve problems in health care and medical research. Her work combined concepts from anatomy, physiology, and neuroscience with electronic technology and electrical engineering.

Estrin designed and implemented a computer system to map the nervous system. Later, she published papers on how to map the brain with the help of computers. She helped design Israel's first computer, the WEIZAC, in 1954. Estrin served as the director of the Data Processing Laboratory at the Brain Research Institute at the University of California, Los Angeles (UCLA), being barred from employment in the School of Engineering at UCLA by nepotism rules since her husband was on the faculty there. After UCLA dropped its nepotism rules in 1980, she was able to become a professor in the computer science department of the School of Engineering and Applied Science.

Not only a pioneer in her technical field, but a pioneer among women engineers, Estrin was the first woman elected to national office in the Institute of Electrical and Electronics Engineers (IEEE) as vice president in 1981. In the late 1970s, she was the first woman to join the board of trustees of The Aerospace Corporation. Her presence and leadership on that board encouraged many women to pursue careers in aerospace engineering. She has been very active in the women's movement, encouraging women to be engineers from the 1970s forward.

Among her many awards are the 1981 SWE Achievement Award "in recognition of her outstanding contributions to the field of biomedical engineering, in particular neurophysiological research through application of computer science." A Fellow of SWE, IEEE, and American Association for the Advancement of Science (AAAS), she is a founding fellow of the American Institute for Medical and Biological Engineering.

Her honorary doctor of science degree from the University of Wisconsin in 1989 included the following citation: "Refusing to be daunted by prejudice, she demonstrated through the undeniable quality of her work that talent is not tied to gender. She has been a model for other women who have entered and enriched the field of engineering, including two of her daughters."[36]

Mildred S. Dresselhaus (1930 -)

The only female recipient of the National Medal of Science in the engineering category to date, Dr. Mildred Dresselhaus has been on the faculty of MIT since 1967. She was the first woman tenured in the School of Engineering at MIT. In August 2000, she became the Director of the Office of Science in the Department of Energy, having been nominated by President Clinton and confirmed by the U.S. Senate.

As an Institute Professor of electrical engineering and physics at MIT (the first woman to be so honored), Dresselhaus is a solid-state physicist and materials scientist, whose research areas include superconductivity; the electronic and optical properties of semimetals, semiconductors, and metals; and particularly, carbon-based materials. The citation for the 1990 National Medal of Science reads, "For her studies of the electronic properties of metals and semimetals, and for her service to the Nation in establishing a prominent place for women in physics and engineering."

Dresselhaus received an A.B. from Hunter College in 1951 in physics and math. She received encouragement to study physics at Hunter from her advisor Rosalyn Yalow (later a Nobel Laureate in medicine) as opposed to becoming a schoolteacher. After a year in Cambridge, England, on a Fulbright scholarship in physics, she studied first at Harvard and then completed her thesis and received her Ph.D. from the University of Chicago in 1958.

The 1977 recipient of SWE's Achievement Award "for significant contributions in teaching and research in solid state electronics and materials engineering," Dresselhaus founded the MIT Women's Forum in 1970. The objective of the forum was to support the careers of women in science and engineering at MIT. In 1999, she received the Nicholson Medal for Humanitarian Science from the American Physical Society "for being a compassionate mentor and lifelong friend to young scientists; for setting high standards as researchers, teachers and citizens; and for promoting international ties in science."

In addition to her sixteen honorary degrees, Dresselhaus has been President of the AAAS, a member of the National Academy of Engineering and the National Academy of Sciences, and a Fellow of SWE, AAAS, IEEE, and others. She attributes her success in balancing her career and raising four children to a supportive husband.[37]

Chapter Five
BRIDGES TO THE FUTURE

Moving Forward in the 1980s

In the early 1980s, Americans began worrying about whether or not the country was on an equal footing with technologically advanced Japan. As a result of this international competitiveness, more focus was placed on engineers and technology in the U.S., in the hopes of keeping America economically in-line. The pipeline for engineers and scientists began to be discussed, and women in engineering began to receive significant focus and recognition.[1]

The Science and Engineering Equal Opportunities Act of 1980 was passed to include women and minorities as problem solvers to deal with the now recognized issues of environment, food shortages, and areas affected by affirmative action. The act said:

> ...it is the policy of the United States to encourage men and women, equally, of all ethnic, racial, and economic backgrounds to acquire skills in science, engineering and mathematics, to have equal opportunity in education, training, and employment in scientific and engineering fields, and thereby to promote scientific and

engineering literacy and the full use of the human
resources of the nation in science and engineering.[2]

Yet in spite of this rhetoric, the Reagan administration cut science education funding in the early 1980s. The falloff in the rate of increase in the
number of women in engineering is evidenced by the flattening of the
number of female graduates through the 1980s, and is attributed, in part,
to cuts in federal funding and the Reagan administration's significantly
reduced emphasis on affirmative action.[3]

Congress became convinced by 1987 that, based on manpower pro-
jections for scientists and engineers that showed significant shortfalls by
2006, something needed to be done. A law was passed creating a Task
Force on Women, Minorities and the Handicapped in Science and
Engineering to examine the current status of those groups in the targeted
fields and to coordinate existing federal programs to promote their education and employment in science and engineering. The Task Force
Report was issued in 1989, and thereafter many more educational institutions established Women in Engineering Programs and Minority
Engineering Programs with the resulting available federal funding. The
task force also reported that non-traditional engineers and scientists faced
barriers in both promotion and progression in their careers.[4]

The latest national imperative to get women and minorities into technology was reflected in a 1988 report:[5]

> If compelled to single out one determinant of U.S. com-
> petitiveness in the era of the global, technology-based
> economy, we would have to choose education, for in
> the end people are the ultimate asset in global compe-
> tition... But an especially important further step will be
> to extend the pool from which the pipeline draws by
> bringing into it more women, more racial minorities,
> and more of those who have not participated because
> of economic, social, and educational disadvantage.
> Thus not only is providing a better grounding in math

and science for all citizens a matter of making good on the American promise of equal opportunity, it is a pragmatic necessity if we are to maintain our economic competitiveness.

Additional legislative and regulatory actions in the 1980s and 1990s helped improve the work force for women. Specifically, the Equal Employment Opportunity Commission issued regulations in 1980 that defined sexual harassment as a form of sex discrimination, thus prohibited under the Civil Rights Act of 1964. U.S. Supreme Court rulings in the 1980s and 1990s further clarified the situations constituting sexual harassment.[6] Women engineers, who tended to be more isolated in work environments because of their low numbers, now had more recourse for some of the more blatant behavior they were experiencing.

The 1990s

In the 1990s, the U.S. was now focused on ways to remain globally competitive with the entire world, not just Japan.[7] More initiatives, task forces, studies, and conferences occurred to further examine what often boils down to the phrase "Why so few?" Why aren't more women pursuing engineering careers? And although many issues have been identified and solutions proposed, the number of women in engineering failed to increase significantly during the 1990s.[8]

National Academy of Engineering

The National Academy of Engineering (NAE) launched an initiative in 1997 to examine and take positive steps on a national scale toward resolving the issue of why so few women are entering the engineering field. A web site was set up and a major conference, the Summit of Women in Engineering, was held in May 1999.[9]

The Commission on the Advancement of Women and Minorities in Science, Engineering and Technology

The Commission on the Advancement of Women and Minorities in Science, Engineering and Technology (CAWMSET), established by Congress in 1998, again examined the issues and potential remedies associated with the low participation of women, minorities, and persons with disabilities in science, engineering, and technology careers. The Commission's report *Land of Plenty* (September 2000) identified issues and made recommendations with regard to pre-college education, access to higher education, professional life, public image, and nation-wide accountability.[10]

Establishment of Women in Engineering Programs

By 1990, many efforts were being made by a variety of groups—some for more than 30 years—to increase the number of women in engineering. Universities had established Women in Engineering Programs (or Women in Science and Engineering Programs) to both recruit more women students into the field and to retain higher percentages of the female students that enrolled.

Recognizing that cooperation could enhance the many ongoing individual efforts of these programs, the Women in Engineering Programs & Advocates Network (WEPAN) was founded in 1990. Its original objective was to effect a positive change in the engineering infrastructure conducive to the academic and professional development of women and men. Its original mission was "to increase the number of women who pursue careers in engineering by encouraging colleges and universities throughout the U.S. to initiate or expand Women in Engineering Programs at the pre-college, undergraduate and graduate levels." The organization has grown to over 500 individuals representing almost 200 institutions, corporations, and non-profit organizations. Its current mission is "to be a catalyst for change that enhances the success of women in the engineering professions."[11]

Minority Women in Engineering

The national focus on increasing the talent pool in engineering has focused on minorities as well as women for many years. As early as 1974, the National Action Council for Minorities in Engineering, Inc. was established to lead national efforts to increase access to careers in engineering and other science-based disciplines for minorities. In 1979, the National Association of Minority Engineering Program Administrators (NAMEPA) was established to promote collaboration and cooperation among the many groups committed to improving the recruitment and retention of African Americans, Hispanics, and Native Americans in the industry. One significant initiative, announced in September 1999, the Gates Millenium Scholars Program, is an activity of the Bill and Melinda Gates Foundation. This 20-year program will provide financial assistance to high-achieving minority students who pursue undergraduate and graduate degrees in technical fields including engineering.[12]

Overall degrees awarded to minority candidates do not reflect the levels of minorities in the general population. However, the proportion of minority women receiving engineering degrees exceeds the percentage of non-minority women in all categories at the B.S. level. In 1999, approximately 30 percent of the college-age population and 25 percent of the entire work force were African Americans, Latinos, and Native Americans. Their percentage of the total engineering degrees awarded at the B.S. level are shown in Table 5-1.[13]

Table 5-1

1999 B.S. Engineering Degrees (Percent of Total)

	Total	Male	Female
All	100.0	80.2	19.8
Non-minority	68.2	82.1	17.9
African American	5.1	65.0	35.0
Hispanic American	6.5	74.0	26.0
Native American	0.5	74.4	25.6
Asian American	11.6	76.5	23.5
Foreign National	8.1	84.4	15.6

For example, African Americans received 5.1 percent of all 1999 B.S. engineering degrees. African-American males constituted 65 percent of the degree recipients and African-American females, 35 percent.

1997 minority degree awards at the M.S. and Ph.D. levels (Table 5-2) provide further evidence of the low percentages of minorities obtaining engineering degrees and the few minorities at the Ph.D. level, who constitute the pool for minority engineering faculty positions.[14]

Table 5-2

1997 M.S. and Ph.D. Engineering Degrees

	M.S.			Ph.D.		
	% of total	Men	Women	% of total	Men	Women
Non-minority	51.6	82.3	17.7	41.5	86.0	14.0
African American	2.5	66.9	33.1	1.4	73.7	26.3
Hispanic American	2.7	76.5	23.5	1.3	86.2	13.8
Native American	0.2	83.1	16.9	0.1	87.5	12.5
Asian American	9.6	75.0	25.0	7.3	82.2	17.8
Foreign Nationals	33.4	82.3	17.7	48.4	90.6	9.4

Selection of Field Specialties

The distribution of women within engineering disciplines is not uniform. Women are more likely to choose industrial and chemical engineering as a specialty, a trend that has now been apparent for many years. In 1999, women received 36 percent of the chemical engineering degrees and 33 percent of the industrial engineering degrees nationwide, compared with their overall rate of 19.8 percent of the total degrees awarded. The largest disciplines, in terms of numbers of degrees awarded in a year and most available jobs, are mechanical/aerospace and electrical/computer engineering, where the percentages of women are the lowest.[15]

Advancement/Promotion/Glass Ceiling

In 1993, women comprised about 12 percent of the employed scientific and engineering labor force in industry. Although this low representation is due in part to the subfields or engineering disciplines selected by women, another significant contributing factor is the attrition rate for women, which is double that for men and substantially higher than for other employment sectors. First, women face limited access to employment opportunities as many recruitment practices are based on the "old boys" network. Then, women engineers find a wide range of less than friendly work practices—especially lower salary and limited opportunities for advancement—and as a result, very few women are in the top levels of corporations.[16]

Many of the issues faced by women engineers with regard to promotion and the glass ceiling are the issues faced by all women in the work force. However, women engineers have many fewer role models and often face a more hostile environment than women in other professions.

More male engineers feel they are part of management as compared to women engineers, and men have fewer layers of authority between themselves and the top than do women. This disparity persists even among groups of men and women matched for age and other variables.[17]

In academic environments, female engineering faculty are much less likely to be full professors than men. In fact, in 1997, 98.6 percent of full professors in engineering were male and only 1.4 percent female. Even at the rank of associate professor, women accounted for only 6.3 percent of total engineering faculty. More women were at the rank of assistant professor at 13.7 percent, but those women had yet to receive tenure. On the non-tenure track, 13.6 percent of engineering instructors/lecturers were female and 15.7 percent of other faculty. Women engineering faculty constitute the lowest percentage of full professors of any field. The percentage of female full professors in the physical sciences is 4.2 percent, and the percentage of female full professors in the computer and math sciences is 6.7 percent.[18]

In the fall of 2000, 11 deans of engineering at U.S. universities were female.[19]

Compensation

For a number of years, data from the College Placement Council have shown that women engineers receive offers for starting salaries at a level as good or better than men. SWE's 1993 National Survey data agree with this finding, and also indicated that before engineers enter their thirties, men begin to outearn women. Men then consistently outearn women, with the gap growing throughout the rest of their careers.[20]

The salaries that engineers earn are dependent on the discipline studied, the type of employer, and years of experience. Average annual salary expectations are not as high as for lawyers or doctors, but compare favorably to business management and surpass mathematicians, psychologists, and architects. Full professors earn a salary higher than the average that would be expected by an engineer in that discipline in non-academic employment, but those salaries are significantly higher than would be achieved by associate and assistant professors, and instructors.[21]

Engineering in the 21st Century

As we look toward the future, and the inevitable globalization of the economy, the U.S. will need all the technical talent it can find. Women are more prevalent today in engineering than they ever have been. However, there is still a lower percentage of women in engineering than in any other professional field.[22] Many issues must be resolved in order for the number of young women pursuing an engineering education to increase significantly.

Entering the twenty-first century, the focus for engineering employees and employers alike is flexibility—being able to adjust to different cultural, national, and workplace settings, developing just-in-time skills, and remaining comfortable with one's gender, race, and ethnicity. Instead of concentrating on larger numbers of engineers (although certainly numbers are still important), the federal government's focus has shifted to a flexible engineering work force, trained with a new engineering curricula:[23]

> ...in the post Cold War there is a change again in the driving forces for engineering education...there is more emphasis and focus on team work, communication, external constraints on design, continuous improvement.... In a tight job market, engineers who have skills that follow this new paradigm are more likely to be employable. They will have a competitive advantage.

And who better to be those flexible engineers than women? Young women must become aware of the many opportunities available for engineers and the tremendous satisfaction that comes from an engineering career. After all, engineers make the world work.

KEY WOMEN OF THIS PERIOD

Sheila Widnall (1938 -)

The first woman placed in charge of a branch of the military, Dr. Sheila Widnall became Secretary of the Air Force in 1993, after she was appointed by President Clinton. She was praised by the president "as a woman of high achievement, a respected scientist, a skilled administrator, and a dedicated citizen." Prior to her service as Secretary, she spent 28 years at the Massachusetts Institute of Technology (MIT), where she had won international acclaim for her work in fluid dynamics. After her resignation from the Air Force, she rejoined the MIT faculty.

Widnall's father fostered her interest in science and math, and her working mother showed her that women can manages a career and a family. She was encouraged to pursue an engineering education. But when she enrolled at MIT, she was one of 23 women out of a total of 936 freshmen. As she had never been part of a minority group, she experienced a culture shock. Despite this initial setback, Widnall received her B.S., M.S., and Ph.D. degrees from MIT in aeronautics and astronautics. Her first child was born six months before she finished her Ph.D. and her second, four years later. She credits a supportive husband and the ability to find good daytime child care (graduate students' wives) as contributors to her career success. She was the first MIT alumna to become a member of the faculty of the School of Engineering. And for many years after she was hired, she was the only woman engineer on faculty. In addition, she was the first woman to head the entire MIT faculty.

Widnall is known internally for her fluid dynamics work involving aircraft turbulence and spiraling airflows. She is the holder of three patents, has a long history of professional activities, and has received many awards. She is a member of the National Academy of Engineering and has received its Distinguished Service Award (1993). In 1998 she received the Institute of Electrical and Electronics Engineers' (IEEE)

Centennial Medal. Widnall received the Society of Women Engineers' (SWE) Achievement Award in 1975 "in recognition of her significant contributions to the fluid mechanics of low speed aircraft and hydrofoils." She has served as President of the American Association for the Advancement of Science (AAAS) and as a trustee for The Aerospace Corporation.

Widnall says, "I believe that women should pursue their interest in science and engineering. The future has a way of taking care of itself if one has the proper education that supports one's dreams."[24]

Eleanor Baum (c. 194? -)

The first female dean of any engineering college in the U.S. and the first female president of the American Society for Engineering Education, Dr. Baum is a Fellow of the Accreditation Board for Engineering and Technology (ABET), IEEE, and SWE. She has also served as the President of ABET.

Baum's route to engineering was not an easy one. Her guidance counselor thought she should study something else. In fact, almost anything else would do. Her mother was very worried that people would think she was strange and, as a result, that no one would marry her. Baum was not accepted at several engineering colleges where she applied for admission because she was female; in at least one case her application was denied due to a lack of women's bathrooms. In the end, she was the only female in her engineering class at City College of New York. She received a B.S. in electrical engineering (1959) and completed her M.S. (1961) and Ph.D. (1964) degrees from the Polytechnic Institute of New York.

Baum is a national leader in engineering education and the advancement of women in science and technology. She was the 1988 recipient of the Emily Roebing Award presented by the National Women's Hall of Fame. She was inducted into the Women in Technology International Hall of Fame in 1996. A recipient of SWE's Upward Mobility Award, Baum serves on the Boards of Directors of several corporations.[25]

Hall of Fame in 1996. A recipient of SWE's Upward Mobility Award, Baum serves on the Boards of Directors of several corporations.[25]

Donna Shirley (1941 -)

Currently Associate Dean for Advanced Program Development at the University of Oklahoma, Donna Shirley burst into the national and international scene in July 1997 when the Mars Pathfinder and its Sojourner Truth Rover—the solar-powered, self-guided, microwave-oven-sized explorer—began their exploration of the Martian surface.

Shirley decided at age 10 to be an aeronautical engineer and to build airplanes. At 15, she began flying lessons and at 16, she soloed. However, her path to aeronautical engineering was not as straight as she might have envisioned.

When Shirley arrived at the University of Oklahoma in 1958 determined to study aeronautical engineering, her first visit with her advisor began with him telling her, "Girls can't be engineers." The school newspaper even ran an article noting the rarity of female engineering students—all six of them. Shirley did eventually graduate in 1962, but with a degree in journalism.

After a stint as a technical writer at McDonnell Aircraft, Shirley reapplied to the University of Oklahoma, took a leave of absence from McDonnnell, and went back to engineering school. In the spring of 1965, she did graduate with a B.S. in aerospace/mechanical engineering. And she returned to McDonnell Aircraft. In 1966, Shirley took a job with the Jet Propulsion Laboratory with one objective: to get to Mars—a goal that would take 31 years.

Inducted into the Women in Technology International Hall of Fame, Shirley has written several books, including her autobiography and a book on using the collective creativity of groups to develop ideas and turn those ideas into real products.[26]

F. Suzanne Jenniches (1948 -)

Suzanne Jenniches, vice president, Communications Systems, Northrop Grumman, had not even heard of the word engineering until she was 23 years old and teaching high school biology. She was influenced by the first Earth Day (April 1970) to enroll in a master's program in environmental engineering at Johns Hopkins University.

In 1978, she completed her M.S. in environmental engineering, although the large majority of her courses were undergraduate courses in computers and electrical engineering. In the interim, Jenniches had left her public education career and begun her employment with Westinghouse Electric Corporation as a product evaluation engineer.

Jenniches rose through the ranks at Westinghouse, at one point becoming the Operations Manager for B-1B Offensive Radar and Special Access Systems. The production of this radar system was the critical path for the B-1B program and was briefed monthly to then-Secretary of Defense Caspar Weinberger. Jenniches successfully introduced the first Electronically Scanned Antenna into a production aircraft with the B-1B.

Subsequently, she became General Manager, Automation and Information Systems, for Westinghouse and later Northrop Grumman (after its purchase of this division of Westinghouse). While in this position, Jenniches oversaw the delivery of over 10,000 postal systems for the U.S. Postal Service. In addition, she led the team that designed and deployed the Federal Express Small Package Sort System in its 500,000-square-foot facility in Memphis, Tennessee. Since 1999, Jenniches has had responsibility for leading Northrop Grumman's efforts in the defense communications systems market.

Jenniches received the 2000 Achievement Award from SWE "in recognition of outstanding leadership in manufacturing innovation and for setting the highest standards of excellence in producibility engineering." She has served as the National President of SWE. Jenniches serves on corporate boards and has received gubernatorial appointments to several Maryland commissions and task forces. A Fellow of SWE, Jenniches has been a consultant to the Service and Technology Board of the U.S. Army since 1989.[27]

Judith Resnik (1949 - 1986)

A member of the ill-fated Challenger mission in 1986, Judith Resnik was a "can do" kind of person. She received her B.S. in electrical engineering from Carnegie-Mellon in 1970 and a Ph.D., also in electrical engineering, from the University of Maryland, College Park, in 1977.

Resnik was selected for the astronaut corps in 1978, having previously served as a biomedical engineer and staff fellow in the laboratory of neurophysiology at the National Institutes of Health. The second American woman to travel in space, Resnik was a mission specialist on space shuttle Discovery's maiden voyage in 1984. During 96 orbits of the Earth, the Discovery deployed three satellites and removed ice particles from the orbiter using the Remote Manipulator System (the robotic arm). Resnik had developed operational procedures and software for the arm. In addition, she developed deployment procedures for a tether satellite system.

Resnik lived life to its fullest. She was a classical pianist and a gourmet cook. She was working on her pilot's license and enjoyed running and riding her bicycle.

SWE established the Resnik Challenger Medal in her memory. It is awarded for visionary contributions to space exploration. SWE also awards Resnik scholarships. The IEEE Judith A. Resnik Award recognizes outstanding contributions to space engineering.[28]

Bonnie Dunbar (1949 -)

Astronaut Dr. Bonnie J. Dunbar is a pioneering engineering woman. When she enrolled as an engineering student at the University of Washington, there were nine women in her entire freshman class. She received B.S. and M.S. degrees in ceramic engineering from the University of Washington in 1971 and 1975, respectively. When she joined the Astronaut Corps in 1980, she was in only the second class at NASA to accept women. Subsequently, she earned her Ph.D. in mechanical/biomedical engineering at the University of Houston in 1983.

Prior to becoming an astronaut, Dunbar was employed as a senior research engineer at Rockwell International Space Division, where she played a key role in the development of the ceramic tiles that form the heat shield for the space shuttle, allowing it to reenter the Earth's atmosphere. In 1978, Dunbar became a payload officer/flight controller for NASA. She served as a guidance and navigation officer/flight controller for the Skylab reentry mission in 1979.

Since becoming an astronaut, Dunbar's NASA technical assignments have included: verification of shuttle flight software; serving as a member of the Flight Crew Equipment Control Board; 13 months in training in Star City, Russia for a 3-month flight on the Russian Space Station, Mir; and Assistant Director with a focus on University Research. She has logged more than 50 days in space.

Her experiments in space have involved protein crystal growth; surface tension physics; and tests on muscle performance, bones, the immune system and the cardio-pulmonary system. Dunbar received the Resnik Challenger Medal from SWE in 1992 and the IEEE Judith Resnik Award in 1993. She has been inducted into the Women in Technology International Hall of Fame.[29]

Sherita Ceasar (1959 -)

Growing up in the "projects" (of the Chicago Housing Authority) may not have been the most auspicious start to an engineering career for Sherita Ceasar, but in high school, Ceasar heard about engineering at a career fair. When the representative from the Illinois Institute of Technology (IIT) asked her if she wanted to make a lot of money after college, she was hooked. She attended an outreach program for minorities after her junior year in high school and placed second in mechanical aptitude out of 250 students. Ceasar was destined to study mechanical engineering.

After a B.S. and M.S. in mechanical engineering from IIT, Ceasar embarked on a career that has since led her to being the highest-ranking black female engineer within Motorola's Paging Products Group and now the Vice President and General Manager, SciCare Subscriber Network Services for Scientific Atlanta.

As Director of Manufacturing at Motorola's Boynton Beach, Florida facility, Ceasar led an organization of nearly 2,000 manufacturing associates, engineers, and managers in the manufacture of alphanumeric and numeric pagers. The facility was named by Arthur D. Little as the "Best of the Best in Manufacturing Management" and Ceasar represented Motorola at Arthur D. Little's "1995 Best of the Best Colloquium on Manufacturing Management."

A past National President of SWE, Ceasar received the 1997 Women of Color in Technology Award and has been inducted into the Women in Technology International Hall of Fame, in addition to numerous other awards. Ceasar's personal motto is, "I am a committed, empowering leader who will make a difference in the world."[30]

APPENDIX

TYPES OF ENGINEERS

Many different types of engineers and fields of engineering exist. This appendix presents a brief overview of the various fields of engineering. Many of the fields are interrelated and grew out of a few basic types of engineering (chemical, civil, electrical, and mechanical).[1]

Aerospace (or aeronautical or astronautical) engineers design, develop, and implement new and existing technologies in airplanes, space vehicles, and helicopters. These engineers are also involved in control and guidance systems, information systems, and instruments used for navigation of aircraft. An engineer in this field can even end up as an astronaut or as the Secretary of the Air Force.

Agricultural engineers become involved in every aspect of food production, including processing, storage, handling, and distribution. An important aspect of the agricultural engineers' job is to maintain or improve the environmental quality of the agro-ecosystem. Agricultural engineers might work in areas that include the genetic manipulation of plants and animals, development of environmentally friendly pesticides, or the production of enzymes for food processing, as well as such traditional areas as design of tractors, barns, drainage systems, harvesters, and processing units.

Architectural engineers work with architects on buildings and focus on safety, costs, constructability, and sound construction methods. They work on building systems including illumination and heating, ventilation, and air conditioning.

Biomedical engineers design, test, and analyze equipment and materials used in treating medical conditions. Such equipment and materials include artificial joints and body parts, surgical tools, scanning equipment, and breathing and heart monitors.

Ceramic engineers work with processes that convert nonmetallic minerals, clay, or silicates to ceramic products, such as the tiles used to deflect heat on the space shuttle.

Chemical engineers plan, design, and operate facilities that take ideas from scientists and translate them into large-scale commercial plants to meet the needs of society. Chemical engineers are employed in many industries, including chemical (including synthetic rubber and fiber), petrochemical, food-processing (including breweries and distilleries), forestry, and pharmaceutical.

Civil engineers plan, design, and construct buildings, dams, airports, water and wastewater treatment and distribution systems, mass transit systems (including roads and bridges), and drainage systems.

Computer engineers design, construct, and operate computer hardware and software systems. Knowledge of electrical engineering and computer science is generally required for computer engineers.

Construction engineers plan and build buildings and other facilities in coordination with engineers from many other disciplines. They are very concerned with the cost of the facilities being built, the timely provision of the needed materials, and the safety of the project.

Electrical/electronic engineers are involved with the production and delivery of electricity, telecommunications, cable, electronics, control systems, and digital systems. Some electrical engineers may be involved in biomedical engineering and digital signal processing.

Engineering management concentrates on preparing engineers for management positions early in their careers through a focus on such areas as research and development, operations and logistics, and quality and process. Courses emphasize broad-based management skills, analytical tools, and practical methods.

Engineering physicists are involved in applying mathematical and physical concepts and developments to many engineering fields.

Environmental engineers design products and systems to solve environmental problems, particularly cleaning up (or keeping clean) the air, water, and land (including cleaning up oil spills in the ocean).

Geological engineers become involved in aspects of discovering and recovering minerals from the earth.

Geotechnical engineers understand the properties of soils and use this knowledge to establish soil bearing capacities to support structures such as dams, foundations of structures, and harbors.

Industrial engineers determine the most effective ways for an organization to use its resources—people, money, and time—to make a product. Industrial engineers are generally concerned about such issues as reliability, optimum performance, cost efficiency, quality control, plant design, and management of human resources.

Manufacturing engineers are involved in all aspects of manufacturing products, from the design of equipment processes and products, to the management of manufacturing facilities. Their concerns include the manufacturing operation itself, quality management, on-time delivery, capacity, and cost.

Marine or ocean engineers design harbors, underwater machines, and off-shore drilling platforms. They specifically take into account the additional factors that must be considered in designing and manufacturing for the ocean environment, including wave motion, currents, temperature variations, and chemical and biological factors.

Materials engineers develop new materials (polymers, ceramics, composites and electronic materials) to meet the needs of products that must withstand conditions such as high pressures or high temperatures. Such materials include alloys for auto engines, airplanes, and spacecraft.

Mechanical engineers design, test and analyze machines, structures, and devices including cars, pumps, heating, ventilation and cooling systems, combustion systems, and sports equipment (such as bicycles and skis). Mechanical engineers get involved in a wide variety of areas including manufacturing, metallurgy and materials, machine design, systems engineering, plant design, construction and operation, environmental engineering, and power and energy.

Metallurgical engineers focus on metals with regard to mining location, ore refining, and part fabrication.

Mining engineers design and plan mining operations such as for coal, gold, bauxite, and copper. Mining engineers have areas of expertise ranging from estimating ore reserves, geostatistics, geology, and underground and surface mine design, to the design of mining equipment, rock and soil mechanics, and mineral processing. One mining engineer, Herbert Hoover, became President of the United States.

Nuclear engineers design, develop, and implement projects relating to the nuclear industry, from nuclear power plants for the electric power industry to nautical propulsion systems for the U.S. Navy. Nuclear engineers are involved in the handling of nuclear fuels used in the commercial and military sectors and the handling of radioactive materials used in hospitals, clinics, laboratories, and military facilities. Jimmy Carter, a nuclear engineer, became President of the United States.

Petroleum engineers are involved in ensuring the discovery, recover, processing, and delivery of oil and gas.

Software engineers develop programs to operate computers and microprocessors.

Structural engineers plan and design bridges, towers, stadiums, drilling platforms, and high-rise buildings. Their job is to ensure the structure is safe, stable, effective, and economical.

Surveying engineers learn to apply and expand the principles of land surveying to ensure that projects are located where they are supposed to be. Today, surveying includes up-to-date technology such as satellites, aerial and terrestrial photogrammetry, and computers.

Systems engineers use logic, mathematics, and science as well as understanding of human and institutional needs, wants, and limitations to design, develop, implement, and control complex large-scale groups of resources and processes to achieve a common objective.

Endnotes

Introduction

1. "American Perspectives on Engineers & Engineering." A "Harris Poll" Pilot Study conducted for the American Association of Engineering Societies, July 1998, pp. 6-9. "Harris Poll Show Engineering Remains a 'Stealth Profession' Among Women and Minorities," Press Release, American Association of Engineering Societies, September 1, 1998, p. 1. In fact, about five percent of the population still think that engineers only operate trains.

2. Skinner, Richard A. and G. Phillip Cartwright, "Higher Education and the Technology Workforce Shortage," www.contract.kent.edu/ change/articles/mayjun98.html, accessed September 15, 2000, p. 2.

3. "For Engineering Education, 1997 Outputs Look Like 1996," *Engineers, Engineering Workforce Commission of the American Association of Engineering Societies,* Volume 4, Number 1, January 1998, p. 12. In 1968, only five women (0.2%) nationwide received an engineering Ph.D. degree. That number had increased to 835 women by 1997 (12.2%). "Koerner, Brendan I., "Where the Boys Aren't," *U.S. News & World Report,* February 8, 1999, pp. 47 and 50.

4. "Number of women studying engineering still growing," *Engineers,*

Engineering Workforce Commission of the American Association of Engineering Societies, Volume 5, Number 2, June 1999, page 4. The source of these data was the National Center for Education Statistics. (A portion of the table is provided at the end of this note.) It is still possible to get a home economics bachelor's degree at colleges, including Fresno City College and The Master's College. Many colleges have changed the name of the curriculum. Both Washington State University and New Mexico State University have a College of Agriculture and Home Economics. Oregon State University has a College of Home Economics and Education. "New Mexico State University College of Agriculture and Home Economics," accessed September 15, 2000.

U.S. Bachelor's Degrees in 1996, All Areas of Study

	Men	Women
Total	522,454	642,338
Home economics	1,885	13,918
Library science	8	50
Health professions	15,432	68,604
Education	26,233	79,276
Psychology	19,817	53,474
Biological sciences	28,849	32,145
Business Management	116,842	110,260
Social sciences and history	65,872	60,607
Mathematics	7,134	6,009
Agriculture	13,535	7,896
Architecture	5,340	3,012
Physical sciences	12,578	7,069
Computer/information sciences	17,468	6,630
Engineering and engineering-related technologies	64,596	12,481
Transportation	3,143	418
ROTC	7	0

5. *Land of Plenty*, Report of the Congressional Commission on the Advancement of Women and Minorities in Science, Engineering and Technology Development, September 2000, pp. 2-6.

6. Gilbreth, Frank B., Jr., and Ernestine Gilbreth Carey, Time Out for Happiness, New York, NY: Thomas Y. Crowell Company, 1970, pp. 188-189. Lillian Moller Gilbreth is more familiarly known as the mother of twelve in the movies and books *Cheaper by the Dozen* and *Belles on Their Toes.*

7. "Rebel with a cause becomes 1st lady dean of engineering," *The National Enquirer*, June 11, 1991, p. 10. "Dr. Eleanor Baum: Dean of Engineering Cooper Union Engineering School," www.witi.com/center/witimuseum/halloffame/previousinducte/1996/dbaum.shtml, accessed July 1, 1999, p. 1.

Chapter One: A Short History of Engineering

1. Ambrose, Susan A., Kristin L. Dunkle, Barbara B. Lazarus, Indira Nair and Deborah A. Harkus, *Journeys of Women in Science and Engineering: No Universal Constants*, Philadelphia: Temple University Press, 1997, pp. 3. "Rediscover Ancient Egypt with Tehuti Research Foundation," www.Egypt-tehuti.com/phyramids.html, accessed September 26, 2000, p. 2. "All About the Great Wall of China," www.enchantedlearning.com/subjects/greatwall/Allabout.html, accessed September 26, 2000. "Grand Canal (Italy)," http://Encarta.msn.com/index/conciseindex/. . ., accessed September 26, 2000. Wright, Kenneth R., Jonathan M. Kelly, Alfredo Valencia Zegarra, "Machu Picchu: Ancient Hydraulic Engineering," Journal of Hydraulic Engineering, October 1997, pp. 838-840. Examples of hydraulic engineering at Machu Picchu include: 1) the cut stone-lined canal was designed for hydraulic and operational efficiency and control of seepage loss and required very little maintenance, 2) infrastructure was designed to maintain the purity of the domestic water supply. Barker, Anne M., "Women in Engineering During

World War II: A Taste of Victory," November 21, 1994, unpublished, Rochester Institute of Technology, p. 13.

2. Ambrose, et.al., op.cit, pp. 4-5. Alic, Margaret, *Hypatia's Heritage: A Short History of Women in Science from Antiquity through the Nineteenth Century*, Boston, Massachusetts: Beacon Press, pp. 22-24.

3. Ambrose, et.al, op.cit., pp. 2-3 and 13. The word engineering is derived from the Latin word ingeniator meaning contriver. It originated only in the 15th century according to the Oxford English Dictionary. The word science is derived from the Latin scientia, knowledge, the present participle of scire, to know. Technology is derived from the Greek *teckne*, meaning skill, art, or craft particularly concerned with methods for effecting certain results.

4. Ibid.

5. "Sir Isaac Newton and Chronology," www.reformation.org/ Newton.html, accessed July 1, 1999, pp 1-2. Wolfson, Richard and Jay M. Pasachoff, *Physics*, Boston, Massachusetts: Little, Brown and Company, 1987, pp. 176-178.

6.   Dutch-born Swiss Daniel Bernoulli described the relationship of fluid speed versus pressure in what became the Bernoulli equation around 1730. He was also responsible for the Bernoulli effect that established the basis for aerodynamic lift, enabling us to fly. Frenchman Andre Marie Ampere formulated the law of electromagnetism in 1820. Some of the basic principles of thermodynamics incorporated in the Carnot cycle and Carnot engine are named after Frenchman Sadi Carnot (1796-1832). Nikola Tesla discovered the rotating magnetic field, the basis of our electricity generation machinery (1884) and the Tesla coil transformer (1891), that allowed the radio industry to develop. Henri Becquerel discovered radioactivity in 1896.   Albert Einstein would put forth his theory of relativity in 1905. "Daniel Bernoulli and the making of the fluid equation," http://pass.maths.org.uk/issue1/bern/index.html, accessed July 1, 1999, p. 3. Wolfson andPasachoff, op.cit., pp. 391 and 393, 486, and 1012. "A Gallery of Electromagnetic Personalities," www.ee.umd.edu/~taylor/frame8.htm, frame3.htm, frame4.htm, and frame7.htm, accessed July 1, 1999. "Tesla, Nikola,"www.neuronet. pitt.edu/~bogdan/tesla/

bio.htm, accessed July 1, 1999, p. 1.

7. Ambrose, et.al., op.cit, pp. 8 and 12. Turner, Edna May, "Education of Women for Engineering in the United States 1885-1952," (dissertation, New York University, 1954), Ann Arbor, Michigan: UMI Dissertation Services, p. 29.

8. Ibid, pp. 8-9, and 13. G. Kass-Simon and Patricia Farnes, Editors. *Women of Science: Righting the Record.* Bloomington, Indiana: Indiana University Press, 1990, p. 147.

9. Barker, op.cit., pp. 13-14. Many early American engineers learned their skills on the job, many of them in civil engineering during the construction of the Erie Canal.

10. Ambrose, et.al., op.cit., p. 13. Turner, op.cit., p. 30. Stephen Van Rensselaer, a very wealthy gentleman with immense land holdings in New York State, was interested in training engineers for the building of canals, roads, and bridges. Rensselaer Polytechnic Institute (RPI) was established at a time when the great masses of people cared little about science. RPI quietly and persistently trained the men who helped make the industrial revolution in the U.S. possible. The first engineering degree from RPI was awarded to a man in 1835; the first degree awarded to a woman was in 1945, 110 years later. Other wealthy industrialists established technical institutes that still bear their names including: Carnegie, Case, Clarkson, Cooper, Drexel, Pratt, Rice, and Stevens.

11. Kass-Simon and Farnes, op.cit., p. 169.

12. Turner, op.cit., p. 29.

13. Rossiter, Margaret W, *Women Scientists in America: Struggles and Strategies to 1940,* Baltimore, Maryland: The Johns Hopkins University Press, 1992, p. 90.

14. Ambrose, et.al., op.cit., p. 14.

15. Rossiter, 1992, op.cit., p. 74.

16. Kass-Simon and Farnes, op.cit., p. 149.

17. Flexner, Eleanor and Ellen Fitzpatrick, *Century of Struggle: The Women's Rights Movement in the United States,* Enlarged Edition, Cambridge, Massachusetts: The Belknap Press of Harvard University, 1996, p. 7. Baer, Judith A., *Women in American Law: The Struggle*

Toward Equality From the New Deal to the Present, 2nd Edition, New York: Homes & Meier, 1996, p. 15.

18.　Along with the law, religion was a potent force in maintaining women's subordinate position. The different religious factions may have disagreed on their religious beliefs and practices, but they never faltered on the one belief they held in common: it was God's will that women should occupy a role secondary to that of men. Flexner and Fitzpatrick, op.cit., p. 8.

19.　Harris, Barbara, *Beyond Her Sphere: Women in the Professions in American History,* Westport, Connecticut: Greenwood Press, 1978, pp. 33-34 and 40-41.

20.　Ambrose, et.al., op.cit., p. 12.

21.　Harris, op.cit., p. 18. Baer, op.cit., pp. 221-222.

22.　Baer, op.cit., p. 20. Flexner and Fitzpatrick, op.cit., pp. 14-15. Garza, Hedda, *Barred From the Bar: A History of Women in the Legal Profession,* New York: Franklin Watts, 1996, p. 21.

23.　Dexter, Elizabeth Anthony, *Career Women of America: 1776-1840,* Francetown, New Hampshire: Marshall Jones Company, 1950, pp. 1-4.

24.　Rossiter, 1992, op.cit., pp. 4-5. *Webster's Dictionary of American Women,* New York: SMITHMARK Publishers, 1996, pp. 661-662.

25.　Rossiter, 1992, op.cit., p. 8. *Webster's,* op.cit., p. 388.

26.　Harris, op.cit., pp. 79-80. Flexner and Fitzpatrick, op.cit., p. 28.

27.　Flexner and Fitzpatrick, op.cit., pp. 73-79.

28.　Harris, op.cit., p. 86. Flexner and Fitzpatrick, op.cit., pp. 26-27.

29.　Harris, op.cit., p. 79 and pp. 98-100. Flexner and Fitzpatrick, op.cit., pp. 28, 30-35, and 116-121. Rossiter, 1992, op.cit., pp. 4-10. Smith College was chartered in 1871 and opened in 1875 with 14 students. *Webster,* op.cit., p. 575.

30.　Barker, op.cit., p. 15. In fact, no woman's college offered an undergraduate engineering curriculum until Smith College announced the establishment of such in 1999 with its expected first graduates in 2004. "Engineers of the Future," *San Francisco Chronicle,* February 26,

1999, page A26.

31. Turner, op.cit., pp. 20 and 50.

32. Harris, op.cit., pp. 98-105. The Morrill Act of 1862 signed into law by President Lincoln gave 10,000 acres of Federal government land to each state to sell and use the proceeds to create a public university to teach agriculture and the mechanic (engineering) arts. The land grant universities today still have the major responsibility for agricultural research and teaching responsibility as well as major "outreach" or extension education mission to the public. "The Land Grant System of Education in the United States," http://www.ag.ohio.state.edu/~ohioline/lines/lgrant.html, accessed April 11, 2000.

33. Shearer, Benjamin H. Shearer and Barbara S. Shearer, Editors, *Notable Women in the Physical Sciences: A Biographical Dictionary*, Westport, Connecticut: Greenwood Press, 1997, pp. 268-270.

34. Alic, op. cit., pp. 41-47. Morrow, Charlene and Teri Perl, Editors, *Notable Women in Mathematics: A Biographical Dictionary*, Westport, Connecticut: Greenwood Press, 1998, pp. 94-97. Hypatia was tortured to death with sharp shells for refusing to convert from paganism to Christianity.

35. Alic, op.cit., pp. 139-147. Morrow and Perl, op.cit., pp. 38-43.

36. Shearer and Shearer, op.cit., pp. 4-8.

37. Morrow and Perl, op.cit., pp. 1-6. Alic, op.cit., pp. 136-139.

38. Morrow and Perl, op.cit., pp. 62-66.

39. Shearer and Shearer, op.cit., pp. 381-385.

40. Morrow and Perl, op.cit., pp. 128-133. Alic, op.cit., pp. 157-163.

Chapter Two: Engineering Education Opens Up for Women

1. G. Kass-Simon and Patricia Farnes, Editors, *Women of Science: Righting the Record*, Bloomington, Indiana: Indiana University Press, 1990, pp. 150-157. Rossiter, Margaret, *Women Scientists in America: Struggles and Strategies to 1940*, Baltimore, Maryland: The Johns

Hopkins University Press, 1992, pp. 30-31 and p. 68.

2. Kass-Simon and Farnes, op.cit., pp. 168-171. LeBold, William K. and Dona J. LeBold, "Women Engineers: A Historical Perspective," *ASEE Prism*, March 1998, p. 31. The U.S. Census of 1890 mentioned 124 women civil engineers and surveyors, but no college records were found for any of them. Barker, Anne M., "Women in Engineering During World War II: A Taste of Victory," November 21, 1994, unpublished, Rochester Institute of Technology, p. 15.

3 LeBold and LeBold, op.cit., p. 30.

4. Rossiter, 1992, op.cit., p. 73.

5. Ibid, p. 73 and pp. 90-91.

6. Barker, op.cit., p. 18.

7. Kass-Simon and Farnes, op.cit., p. 147.

8. Barker, op.cit., p. 17.

9. "An Overview of the United Engineering Foundation: History," www.uefoundation.org/overview.html, accessed December 15, 2000, p. 1. "Founder Societies of the United Engineering Foundation," www.uefoundation.org/fndsoc.html, accessed December 15, 2000. "Historical Highlights," www.idis.com/aime/history.htm, accessed December 15, 2000, pp. 1 and 4. The United Engineering Foundation, founded as the United Engineering Society in 1904 with the generous support of Andrew Carnegie, had the objective of providing a united home for the major engineering societies of the day. The Engineering Societies Building, the first home, was completed in 1906. In 1915, the Engineering Societies Library was formed. It is now part of the Linda Hall Library of Kansas City.

10. "ASCE Profile," www.asce.org/aboutasce/profile.html, accessed December 15, 2000, p. 1. "150 Years of Civil Engineering," www.asce.org/150/1506years.html, accessed December 15, 2000, p. 1. Kass-Simon and Farnes, op.cit., p. 172 and pp. 177-178. Rossiter, 1992, op.cit., p. 389. "Elsie Eaves – Pioneer from the West," SWE Newsletter, May 1959, p. 3.

11. "Historical Highlights," op.cit., pp. 1 and 2. Rossiter, 1992, op.cit., p. 91. "WAAIME," www.idis.com/aime/WAAIME.HTM, accessed

December 19, 2000. The Women's Auxiliary focuses on education and securing and maintaining scholarship funds for assisting young people in obtaining a degree in mining, metallurgical, and petroleum engineering or allied fields.

12. "The History of ASME International," www.asme.org/history /asmehist.html, accessed December 15, 2000, p. 1. Rossiter, 1992, op.cit., p. 91. LeBold and LeBold, op.cit., p. 31. Ingels, Margaret, "Petticoats and Slide Rules," *Western Society of Engineers,* September 4, 1952, and later published in *Midwest Engineer,* p. 14.

13. "The Origins of IEEE," www.ieee.org/organizations/. . .ical_articles/history_of_ieee.html, accessed December 15, 2000, p.1. Edith Clarke's address in 1926 was titled "Steady-State Stability in Transmission Systems." Read, Phyllis J., and Bernard L. Witlieb, *The Book of Women's Firsts,* New York: Random House, 1992, p. 91. Rossiter, 1992, op.cit., p. 389. Kass-Simon and Farnes, op.cit., p. 167. Rossiter, Margaret W., *Women Scientists in America: Before Affirmative Action 1940-1972,* Baltimore, Maryland: The Johns Hopkins University Press, 1995, p. 308. "Welcome to the IEEE Fellow Program: Our History," www.ieee.org/about/awards/fellows/fellows.htm, accessed December 19, 2000, p. 1. Edith Clarke received the Society of Women Engineers' Achievement Award in 1954 "In recognition of her many original contributions to stability theory and circuit analysis." Goff, Alice C., *Women Can Be Engineers,* Ann Arbor, Michigan: Edwards Brothers, Inc., 1946, pp. 215-227. Mabel Rockwell received the Society of Women Engineers' Achievement Award in 1958 "In recognition of her significant contributions to the field of electrical control systems." www.swe.org/SWE/Awards/achieve3.htm, accessed September 1, 1999, pp. 17-19.

14. "A brief history of AIChE," www.aiche.org/welcome/history.htm, accessed August 20, 1999. Rossiter, 1995, op.cit., p. 308. www.swe.org, op.cit., p. 18. Margaret Hutchinson received the Society of Women Engineers' Achievement Award in 1955 "In recognition of her significant contributions to the field of chemical engineering."

15. www.tbp.org/TBP/INFORMATION/Info_book/membership,

accessed August 20, 1999, p. 1. "Tau Beta Pi: Integrity and Excellence in Engineering," www.tbp.org, accessed August 20, 1999. "The Phi Beta Kappa Society: A Short History of Phi Beta Kappa," www.pbk.org/history.htm, accessed December 19, 2000, p. 1. Ingels reports that Catherine Cleveland (Mrs. H.L.) Harelson, University of Kentucky, mechanical engineering, 1924, was awarded the Tau Beta Pi Badge No. 1 for women in 1934 because she made the highest grades ever earned in the engineering college. Ingels, op.cit., p. 19.

16.   Schneider, Dorothy and Carl F. Schneider, *The ABC-CLIO Companion to Women in the Workplace*, Santa Barbara, California: ABC-CLIO, Inc., 1993, p. 81. Ingels, op.cit., pp. 17-18.

17.   "Society History," www.asse.org/hsoci.htm, accessed December 19, 2000, p.1. Rossiter, 1995, op.cit., p. 308.

18   The Outlook for Women in Architecture and Engineering, Bulletin of the Women's Bureau No. 223-5, Washington, DC: U.S. Government Printing Office, 1948, p. 5-33.

19.   Read and Witlieb, op.cit., pp. 358-359. Rossiter, 1995, op.cit., p. 308.

20.   www.iienet.org/Aboutg.htm, accessed August 20, 1999, p. 1. "About the NAE, www.nae.edu/nae/naehome.nsf/weblinks/NAEW-4NHMQM?opendocument, accessed December 19, 2000. Rossiter, 1992, op.cit., p. 389. www.iienet.org/historg.htm, accessed August 20, 1999.

21.   Marion Sara Parker graduated in 1895 from the University of Michigan and worked as a structural engineer for ten years until she married in 1905. LeBold and LeBold, op.cit., p. 31. Kindya, Marta Navia, *Four Decades of the Society of Women Engineers*, New York: Society of Women Engineers, 1990, p. 7. Florence Caldwell (married Frank Jones in 1901) graduated in civil engineering from Colorado School of Mines in 1898. "Brief History of Women at CSM," www.mines.edu/Academic/affairs/wisem/history1.html, accessed December 20, 2000, p. 1. Minette Frankenburger graduated in civil engineering from the University of Colorado in 1903. Huckenpahler, Helen and Donald Morgan, "Women of the Orange Tassel," *Colorado Engineer*, March 1958, pp. 14-55 and

ff. Rossiter, 1992, op.cit., p. 136.

22. Schneider and Schneider, op.cit., p. 81. Meade, Jeff, "Ahead of Their Time: A Century Ago, Women Engineers Such as the Brilliant Bertha Lamme Blazed a Lonely Trail," *ASEE Prism*, January 1993, p. 29.

23. Rossiter, 1992, op.cit., pp. 30-31. Shearer, Benjamin H. Shearer and Barbara S. Shearer, Editors, *Notable Women in the Physical Sciences: A Biographical Dictionary*, Westport, Connecticut: Greenwood Press, 1997, pp. 327-333. Oglivie, Marilyn Bailey, *Women in Science: Antiquity through the Nineteenth Century, a Biographical Dictionary with Annotated Bibliography*, Cambridge, Massachusetts: MIT Press, 1993, pp. 149-152. Kass-Simon and Farnes, op.cit., pp. 150-157. *Webster's Dictionary of American Women*, New York: SMITHMARK Publishers, 1996, pp. 515-516. Read and Witlieb, op.cit., pp. 366-367. "Ellen Richards," www.greatwomen.org/rchrdse.htm, accessed May 26, 1999. Smith College did award Richards an honorary doctorate in 1910.

24. Weigold, Marilyn, Silent Builder: *Emily Warren Roebling and the Brooklyn Bridge*, Port Washington, NY: Associated Faculty Press, Inc., 1984, pp. 50-57 and 145. Kass-Simon and Farnes, op.cit., pp. 171-173. "Landmarks of the World: Brooklyn Bridge," Holiday, June 1959, The Curtis Publishing Company, pp. 125-129.

25. Lee, Erma Conkling, Editor, *The Biographical Encyclopaedia of American Women*, New York: The Franklin W. Lee Publishing Company, Volume II, 1925, pp. 25-29. Ingels, op.cit., p. 11.

26. Bartels, Nancy, "The First Lady of Gearing," www.geartechnology.com/mag/gt-kg.htm, accessed September, 2, 1999, pp. 1-6. Kass-Simon and Farnes, op;cit., p. 168. *Webster*, op.cit., pp. 237-238. Read and Witlieb, op.cit., pp. 176-177. LeBold, and LeBold, op.cit., p. 30.

27. Kass-Simon and Farnes, op.cit., pp. 168-171. LeBold and LeBold, op.cit., p. 31. Meade, op.cit., pp. 27-29. Benjamin Garver Lamme rose to the position of chief engineer at Westinghouse and was in charge of the design of the turbogenerators at Niagara Falls in that historic development. The American Society for Engineering Education has a Lamme Award named for Benjamin. Ingels, op.cit., p. 12.

28. Read and Witlieb, op.cit., pp. 418-419. Ingels, op.cit., p. 13.

Chapter Three: War's Unintended Consequences

1. Barker, Anne M., "Women in Engineering During World War II: A Taste of Victory," November 21, 1994, unpublished, Rochester Institute of Technology, pp. 25-26.

2. LeBold, William K., and Dona J. LeBold, "Women Engineers: A Historical Perspective," *ASEE Prism*, March 1998, pp. 31.

3. Goff, Alice C., *Women Can Be Engineers*, Ann Arbor, Michigan: Edwards Brothers, Inc., 1946, p. iii.

4. Barker, op.cit., p. 26. After the war, a national program of vocational education was established, freeing engineering schools to concentrate on advanced training for undergraduates and graduate degrees as well.

5. Turner, Edna May, "Education of Women for Engineering in the United States 1885-1952," (dissertation, New York University, 1954), Ann Arbor, Michigan: UMI Dissertation Services, pp. 60-61. Based on her survey of engineering colleges, 45 women had graduated with engineering degrees in the 25 years prior to 1919. However, she also notes that the records are incomplete prior to 1920 due to the lack of registrars, office personnel suitable for the work. Hilda Counts Edgecomb, electrical engineer and 1919 graduate of the University of Colorado, compiled a list of more than 120 women engineers employed during World War I.

6. Goff, op.cit., p. iii. Alice Goff states "By an irony of fate, war, always bitterly denounced by women, has advanced them in the engineering profession." Alice Goff was a 1915 graduate of the University of Michigan with a B.S. in civil engineering. She benefited from this irony of war. Goff was employed by a steel company where she appraised, designed, and estimated concrete for large buildings. One of her significant projects was a $15 million bomber assembly plant in Texas. LeBold and LeBold, op.cit., p. 31. Ingels, Margaret, "Petticoats and Slide Rules," *Western Society of Engineers*, September 4, 1952, and later published in *Midwest Engineer*, pp. 14-15. Hazel Irene Quick also graduated from the University of Michigan in 1915 with a degree in civil engineering. In

1916, Margaret Ingels graduated in mechanical engineering from the University of Kentucky. Dorothy Tilden Hanchett received a B.S. in civil engineering in 1917 from the University of Michigan.

    7. Rossiter, Margaret W., *Women Scientists in America: Struggles and Strategies to 1940*, Baltimore, Maryland:The Johns Hopkins University Press, 1992, p. 116.

    8. Ibid., pp. 134-136. *American Men of Science* reported on over 9,000 males in the scientific professions in 1921. Of those 9,036 men, 882 are reported to be engineers. By 1938, the total number of men scientists are reported at 25,375 of which 3,500 are engineers. By 1938, the number of women engineers is reported as eight. The total male population of the U.S. in 1920 (ages 25 to 65) was 25 million that grew to 33 million by 1940. Schneider, Dorothy and Carl F. Schneider, *The ABC-CLIO Companion to Women in the Workplace*, Santa Barbara, California: ABC-CLIO, Inc., 1993, p. 81.

    9. Kindya, Marta Navia, *Four Decades of the Society of Women Engineers*, New York: Society of Women Engineers, 1990, p. 9.

    10. Ibid., p. 10.

    11. Turner, op.cit., p. 61. Turner reports the first master's degree in engineering awarded to a woman was in 1919 by MIT. The woman was Edith Clarke profiled at the end of the chapter.

    12. Barker, op.cit., p. 29.

    13. LeBold and LeBold, op.cit., p. 31.

    14. Barker, op.cit., pp. 31-32. Turner, op.cit., pp. 61-63. The six schools that admitted women only to graduate study were California Institute of Technology, Lehigh University, Union College, Stevens Institute of Technology, Yale University, and Polytechnic Institute of Brooklyn. In addition, Harvard University did not admit women but did allow women students at Radcliffe, an affiliated college, to take courses at Harvard for M.S. and Ph.D. degrees.

    15. Rossiter, 1992, op.cit., p. 136. The National Roster actually found 144 women engineers nationwide in 1941. Rossiter, Margaret W., *Women Scientists in America: Before Affirmative Action 1940-1972*, Baltimore, Maryland: The Johns Hopkins University Press, 1995, p. 14.

16. The Outlook for Women in Architecture and Engineering, Bulletin of the Women's Bureau No. 223-5, Washington, DC: U.S. Government Printing Office, 1948, pp. 5-12 – 5-14.

17. The Outlook. . . , op.cit., p. 5-13.

18. Barker, op.cit., p. 32.

19. LeBold and LeBold, op.cit., p. 32. Rossiter, 1995, op.cit., p. 15.

20. Barker, op.cit., pp. 7 and 9.

21. Barker, op.cit., pp. 7-9. One ready source of female labor was from the curtailment of female-intensive industries unnecessary to the war effort, the largest being silk hosiery manufacturing. The Women's Bureau of the U.S. Department of Labor developed a policy regarding the order in which women should be employed: unemployed women workers displaced by manufacturing changes, girls from high school and college, then homemakers (presumably meant to include older women), and finally mothers of small children as a last resort. By July 1943, there were 17.7 million women in the civilian labor force; there had been 13.9 million in June 1940.

22. Bix, Amy Sue, " 'Engineeresses' 'Invade' Campus: Four Decades of Debate over Technical Coeducation," Proceedings of the 1999 International Symposium on Technology and Society—Women and Technology: Historical, Societal, and Professional Perspectives, 195-201, New Brunswick, NJ, July 29-31, 1999. p. 195. Rossiter, 1995, op.cit., p. 12 and p. 14.

23. Rossiter, 1995, op.cit., p. 12-13. However, even Yost expressed surprise in her preface to *American Women of Science* that women had already done so much: "But I had not the slightest idea that American women of science had achieved even a fractional part of what they have actually accomplished. I was completely unprepared for what a little specialized research began to uncover. So, it seems, was everybody else. When we signed the contract, both my publisher and I knew there was material available for a pretty good book but we had no idea the achievements recorded would be of the caliber they actually are."

24. Bix, op.cit., pp. 195-196. LeBold and LeBold, op.cit., p. 32. Rossiter, 1995, op.cit., pp. 13-16. "The Outlook. . ." op.cit., p. 5-18.

Also Drexel Institute of Technology, Case School of Applied Science, and Stevens Institute of Technology. Barker, op.cit., p. 45.

25. Rossiter, 1995, op.cit., p. 14.

26. Barker, op.cit., pp. 36-37. Rossiter, 1995, op.cit., p. 15. At first, in the 1941-1942 fiscal year, the program was set up as the Engineering, Science and Management Defense Training (ESMDT). But when the U.S. entered the war, the name was changed to Engineering, Science and Management War Training (ESMWT).

27. Barker, op.cit., p. 37.

28. Rossiter, 1995, op.cit., p. 15. The women's colleges included Hunter, Simmons, Smith, Wellesley, Vassar, Bryn Mawr, and Wilson. Language in the program's appropriation read that "no trainee . . . shall be discriminated against because of sex, race, or color."

29. Barker, op.cit., pp. 38-39.

30. Rossiter, 1995, op.cit., p. 15.

31. Barker, op.cit., p. 39.

32. Ibid., p. 40.

33. Bix, op. cit., p. 196.

34. Barker, op.cit., p. 50.

35. Ibid., pp. 46-48.

36. LeBold and Lebold, op.cit., p. 32. Bix, op.cit., p. 196-197. Purdue, Cornell, Texas, Iowa State, and Minnesota already had women enrolled, at least in some curriculum, if not engineering. However, RPI had not had women students on campus for over 100 years and thus experienced quite a culture shock. After the end of World War II, RPI did not revert to being all-male and during the late 1940s had about forty women on campus each year among four thousand men. Through the early 1970s, RPI capped the number of females; there was unofficially a policy of limiting female freshmen to about 140. Barker, op.cit., p. 48.

37. Barker, op.cit., p. 50.

38. Rossiter, 1995, op.cit., p. 14.

39. Barker, op.cit., p. 34.

40. Rossiter, 1995, pp. 9-11. Barker, op.cit., p. 44.

41. Barker, op.cit., p. 51.

42. LeBold and LeBold, op.cit., p. 32. Barker, op.cit., p. 53.

43. Rossiter, 1995, op.cit., pp. xv-xviii and pp. 36-37.

44. Ibid., pp. 30-32. The Serviceman's Readjustment Act of 1944 (commonly known as the GI Bill) included educational provisions offering honorably discharged veterans whose schooling, college, or professional education had been interrupted by military service up to five years of full tuition plus a subsistence allowance at the college of their choice (a very important provision, this last). The nation's 400,000 women veterans were also eligible for these benefits, but were often overlooked. In the post-World War II period, quotas and enrollment restrictions on women at colleges and universities enabled male veterans to displace female applicants. In a short period of time, men had also displaced female staff and faculty. For example, during the wartime, women had constituted 50% of enrollment at Cornell University. Through quotas, that number was pared to 20% of the 1946 enrollment.

Women Earning Undergraduate Engineering Degrees 1948-1953

Year	Number of Degrees
1947-48	191
1949-50	171
1951-52	60
1952-53	37

45. Ibid., pp. 27 and 31-35. One dean of women at Indiana University, without warning or advance consultation, was simply ousted from her office, demoted, and given a much lesser title by the new dean, a former military officer. Nepotism rules that had been relaxed during the War were reinstated leading to the dismissal of employed spouses (almost always the wives) of university employees. Faculty women who married immediately lost their jobs. Barker, op.cit., pp. 2-4.

46. The Outlook. . ., op.cit., p. 5-21.

47. Rossiter, 1995, op.cit., pp. 29-30 and 380. Employment Opportunities for Women in Professional Engineering, Women's Bureau

Bulletin No. 254, Washington, DC: U.S. Government Printing Office, 1954, pp. 13-14. American Men of Science was renamed American Men and Women of Science in 1971. The Society of Women Engineers estimates that there were approximately 6,000 women doing engineering work across the U.S. at the end of World War II, many of them with engineering degrees. Kindya, op.cit., p. 5. Barker, op.cit., p. 57.

Estimate of Number of Employed Women Classified as Engineers, by Selected Age and Education Groups, 1950

Age and Education	Number	Percent
Total women reported as employed	6,475	100
Women 20 years of age and over with 4 or more years of college	2,650	41
Women 25 years of age and over with 1 to 3 years of college	975	15
Women 20 to 24 years of age with 1 to 3 years of college	170	3
Women 20 years of age and over with 4 years of high school	1,280	20
Women with less than 4 years of high school, or 14 to 19 years of age (1,142) or with years of school not reported (245)	1,400	22

Source: U.S. Department of Commerce, Bureau of Census.

48. Kindya, op.cit., p. 10.
49. LeBold and LeBold, op. cit., p. 32.
50. The Outlook . . ., op.cit., p. 5-22. On page 5-75 of this Bulletin from the Women's Bureau are the requirements for membership in the various categories for the principal engineering organizations. Although these requirements may not seem onerous for women today, at the time, most women did not continue their employment once they were married

and many could either not find employment or did not have the opportunity to retain the requisite experience to be promoted and get "responsible engineering experience."

Minimum Requirements for Membership in the Principal Engineering Organizations
American Institute of Chemical Engineers
Regular member
Age: 30 years or over.
Experience: 5 to 10 years in practice or teaching of chemical technology depending upon education with specifications as to number of years of responsible directing works.
Associate member
Age: 21 to 30 years.
Experience or education: Bachelor's degree in chemical engineering or any other bachelor's degree plus 1 year experience in chemical technology or 5 years experience in chemical technology.
American Society of Civil Engineers
Regular member
Age: 35 years or over.
Experience: 12 years experience in engineering or architecture for 5 years of which he must have been in responsible charge of important work proving ability to conceive and design engineering works as well as to direct them.
Associate member
Age: 27 years or more.
Experience or education: 8 years in engineering or architecture proving ability to direct engineering works.
Junior member
Age: 20-33 years.
Experience or education: 4 years or recognized degree in engineering qualifying for subprofessional work.

American Institute of Electrical Engineers

Regular member

Age: 27 years or over.

Experience: 5 years in practice of electrical engineering or the teaching of electrical engineering or electrical science or as a qualified executive or scientific contributor in electrical or closely allied work.

Associate member

Age: 21 years or more.

Experience or education: Currently employed as an electrical engineer or teacher of electrical subjects or doing responsible work with an electrical enterprise.

American Society of Mechanical Engineers

Regular member

Age: 30 years or over.

Experience: 9 years in engineering or teaching of which 3 must have been in responsible charge of work showing ability to design as well as direct important work.

Associate member

Experience or education: Graduation from a recognized school of engineering or the equivalent.

American Institute of Mining and Metallurgical Engineers

Regular member

Age: 27 years or over.

Experience: 6 years in practice of engineering, mining, geology, metallurgy, or chemistry, 3 years of which must have been in responsible charge of work.

Associate member

Age: Not specified.

Experience or education: Interested in or connected with mining, geology, metallurgy, or chemistry.

Junior member

Age: Under 33 years at time of application.

Experience or education: Qualified to hold subprofessional job in one of the fields indicated above.

National Society of Professional Engineers

Regular member

Registration: Registration as a professional engineer in the State in which he resides or practices. Usual State requirements are 8 years of practical experience in professional engineering or graduation from an approved engineering school plus 4 years practice in engineering and the passing of an examination.

51.   Kindya, op.cit., pp. 11-12. Rossiter, 1995, op.cit.,p. 51. "General Information About SWE – Society of Women Engineers," www.swe.org/SWE/Atlarge/swe_info.htm#origins, accessed September 1, 1999, p.1.

52.   Kindya, op. cit., pp. 14-15.

53.   Ibid., pp. 14 and 71. www.swe.org/SWE/Awards/achieve3.htm, accessed September 1, 1999, pp. 17-20.

54.   Rossiter, 1995, op.cit., p. 51. Four articles from *The New York Times* during this period are neutral in tone and present an objective if not fairly bright picture of women in engineering. Beatrice Hicks, President of the Society of Women Engineers (SWE), is quoted, "The present desperate shortage of trained people trained [sic] in engineering will continue to grow and the needed personnel will be drawn from those having engineering aptitudes, whether men or women." "Women Engineers See Field Widening," *The New York Times*, March 11, 1951, p. 47. Dr. John B. Russell, professor of electrical engineering at Columbia University stated, "During the war the number of women working in the field increased substantially and they did a very able job. The current need will result in far greater opportunities for women to study and to practice engineering than in the past." "U.S. Agencies Seek Women Engineers," *The New York Times*, March 12, 1951, p. 19. The results of the election of the Society's officers were reported in "Again Heads Women Engineers," *The New York Times*, August 6, 1951, p. 14. SWE's annual convention was the focus of an article "Women Could Fill Engineering Jobs: Trade Society, Meeting Here, Told They Represent Untapped 'Source of Qualified Talent,'" *The New York Times*, March 16,

1952, p. 79. The article stated that "at present, only three of every thousand practicing engineers are women."

55. Shearer, Benjamin F. and Barbara S. Shearer, Editors, *Notable Women in the Physical Sciences*, Westport, Connecticut: Greenwood Press, 1997, pp. 292-297. Oglivie, Marilyn Bailey, *Women in Science: Antiquity through the Nineteenth Century*, a Biographical Dictionary with Annotated Bibliography, Cambridge, Massachusetts: MIT Press, 1993, pp. 146-147. Read, Phyllis J., and Bernard L. Witlieb, *The Book of Women's Firsts*, New York: Random House, 1992, p. 339. Goff, op.cit., pp. 183-214.

56. *Cheaper by the Dozen*, written by Frank B. Gilbreth, Jr. and Ernestine Gilbreth Carey, chronicles the adventures of growing up in a household of twelve children whose parents are efficiency experts. Gilbreth, Frank B., Jr. and Ernestine Gilbreth Carey, *Time Out For Happiness*, New York, NY: Thomas Y. Crowell Company, 1970. LeBold and LeBold, op.cit., ,p. 31. Kindya, op.cit., pp. 14 and 18. Kass-Simon, G., and Patricia Farnes, Editors, *Women of Science: Righting the Record*, Bloomington, Indiana: Indiana University Press, 1990, pp. 157-164. Goff, op.cit., pp. 116-132. The Hoover Medal is conferred upon an engineer whose professional achievements and personal endeavors have advanced the wellbeing of mankind. It is administered by a board representing the Founder Societies: ASME, ASCE, AIChE, AIME, and IEEE. Her citation read: "Renowned engineer, internationally respected for contributions to motion study and to recognition of the principle that management engineering and human relations are intertwined; courageous wife and mother; outstanding teacher, author, lecturer and member of professional committees under Herbert Hoover and four successors. Additionally, her unselfish application of energy and creative efforts in modifying industrial and home environments for the handicapped has resulted in full employment of their capabilities and elevation of their self-esteem." "Nominations accepted for prestigious Hoover Medal," ASMENEWS, www.asmenews.org/features/hoover.html, accessed December 20, 2000. "Past Hoover Medal Recipients," www.asme.org/member/awards/hoover_medal/past.html, accessed

December 20, 2000, p. 3. Perusek, Anne, "The First Lady of Engineering," *SWE: Magazine of the Society of Women Engineers,* January/February 2000, pp. 82-83.

57. Clarke graduated Phi Beta Kappa from Vassar in mathematics and astronomy. Kass-Simon and Farnes, op.cit., pp. 164-168. Goff, op.cit., pp. 50-65.

58. Goff, op. cit., pp. 3-18. She received Design patent 72,763 on May 31, 1927 for the Design for a Plate (the china for the railroad). On November 27, 1928, she received Patent 1,693,108 for a ventilator (usually called the Dennis ventilator). "150 People Who Shaped the Way We Live," *The Baltimore Sun 150th Anniversary Publication,* May 17, 1987, p. 184. Design Patent 72,763, United States Patent Office, Patented May 31, 1927. Patent 1,693,108, United States Patent Office, Patented November 27, 1928.

59. Goff, op.cit., p. 77-81. Kass-Simon and Farnes, op.cit., pp. 177-178. "SWE's first fellow members: their achievements and careers," *U.S. Woman Engineer,* December 1980, p. 9. When she retired in May 1963, the *Engineering News-Record* wrote: "It is striking that for more than 30 years the one person who has known more than any other about the statistics of the construction industry in the United States has been a woman, and a remarkable one indeed. She is Elsie Eaves. . ." "Elsie Eaves: Woman Wins Praise in Man's World," *The Colorado Alumnus,* May 1963, p. 8. "Elsie Eaves Scores Again: Is First Woman Honored with ASCE Life Membership," *McGraw-Hill News-Bulletin,* March 15, 1962, p. 6. She also held a Women's Badge from Tau Beta Pi.

60. Ibid., pp. 45-49. www.swe.org/SWE/Awards/achieve3.htm, accessed September 1, 1999, p. 19. "Elsie MacGill," www.ontario2000.on.ca./engl...eatmoments/scitech/macgill_sum.htm, accessed December 21, 2000. "Elizabeth M.G. MacGill," http://collections.ic.gc.ca/high_flyers/macgill.htm, accessed December 21,2000. "Elizabeth "Elsie" MacGill 1905-1980," www.corpserve.nrc. ca.corpserve/hall/u_il4_e.html, accessed December 21, 2000.

61. Candee, Margorie Dent, Editor, *Current Biography,* New York, NY: The H. W. Wilson Company, 1957, pp. 255-257. www.swe.org,

op.cit., p. 15. Stanley, Autumn, *Mothers and Daughters of Invention: Notes for a Revised History of Technology*, New Brunswick, NJ: Rutgers University Press, 1995, p. 386. Her husband was Rodney D. Chipp. The Society of Women Engineers awards as merited the Rodney D. Chipp Memorial Award to a man or company who has supported the advancement and achievement of women in engineering, named in honor of Hicks's husband.

Chapter Four:Suburbia and Sputnik

1. Rossiter, Margaret W., *Women Scientists in America: Before Affirmative Action 1940-1972*, Baltimore, Maryland: The Johns Hopkins University Press, 1995, pp. 50-51. Barker, Anne M., "Women in Engineering During World War II: A Taste of Victory," November 21, 1994, unpublished, Rochester Institute of Technology, p. 58.

2. Employment Opportunities for Women in Professional Engineering, Women's Bureau Bulletin No. 254, Washington, DC: U.S. Government Printing Office, 1954, p.3. At this point in the U.S., production of jet aircraft for civilian passenger service had not even begun. The information is from the Fourth Quarterly Report in 1951 of Defense Mobilizer Wilson.

3. Ibid., p. 9. NSPE surveyed 495 employers who had 3,948 plants.

4. Rossiter, 1995, op.cit., pp. 52-53. Employment Opportunities..., op.cit., p. 9.

5. Rossiter, 1995, op.cit., p. 54.

6. "Engineering Degrees, 1996: Numbers of Women, Minority Graduates Reach All-Time Highs," *Engineers: A Quarterly Bulletin on Careers in the Profession, Engineering Workforce Commission of the American Association of Engineering Societies*, Volume 3, Number 1, January 1997, p. 6.

Women Engineering Graduates 1954-1959					
Year	**B.S.**		**M.S.**		**Ph.D.**	
	Number	Percent	Number	Percent	Number	Percent
1954	62	0.3	13	0.3	1	0.2
1955	62	0.3	13	0.3	0	0.0
1956	76	0.3	19	0.4	0	0.0
1957	81	0.3	15	0.3	1	0.2
1958	109	0.3	20	0.4	4	0.6
1959	121	0.3	24	0.4	1	0.1

7.   Rossiter, 1995, op.cit., p. 55. Turner, Edna May, "Education of Women for Engineering in the United States 1885-1952," (dissertation, New York University, 1954), Ann Arbor, Michigan: UMI Dissertation Services, p. 159. Universities awarding their first engineering degrees to women in the early 1950s included: Utah State Agricultural College, 1950; Brown University, 1951; George Washington University, 1951; University of Florida, 1951; and Saint Louis University, 1952.

8.   Rossiter, 1995, op.cit., p. 32.

9.   Employment Opportunities..., op.cit., p. 5.

10.   Harris, Barbara, *Beyond Her Sphere: Women in the Professions in American History*, Westport, Connecticut: Greenwood Press, 1978, p. 165.

11.   LeBold, William K. and Dona J. LeBold, "Women Engineers: A Historical Perspective," *ASEE Prism*, March 1998, p. 32.

12.   Rossiter, 1995, op.cit., pp. 57-60.

13.   Lucena, Juan C., "'Women in Engineering' A History and Politics of a Struggle in the Making of a Statistical Category." Proceedings of the 1999 International Symposium on Technology and Society—Women and Technology: Historical, Societal, and Professional Perspectives, 185-194. New Brunswick, NJ, July 29-31, 1999., pp. 185-186. Rossiter, 1995, op.cit., p. 61.

14.   Lucena, op.cit., p. 186.

15.   Ibid, p. 186. Rossiter, 1995, op.cit., pp. 96-98.

16.   Lucena, op.cit., p. 186. Rossiter, 1995, op.cit., p. 61.

17. Rossiter, 1995, op.cit., pp. 62-63 and p. 78.

18. Lucena, op.cit., p. 186. Rossiter, 1995, op.cit., p. 63. Most Russian women engineers were married and mothers although journalists in the U.S. tended to portray them as unattractive (plain and stocky) and added insult to injury by commenting that an American woman should be relieved that their country wasn't yet so badly off that she had to be an engineer!

19. Lucena, op.cit., p. 187.

20. LeBold and LeBold, op.cit., p. 32.

21. Harris, op.cit., pp. 167-168.

22. Ibid., pp. 165-166.

23. Ibid., p. 166.

24. Rossiter, 1995, op.cit., p. 14. Harris, op.cit., pp. 174-175. Read, Phyllis J., and Bernard L. Witlieb, *The Book of Women's Firsts*, New York: Random House, 1992, pp. 342-343 and p. 419.

25. The Equal Pay Act was signed in June 1963 by President Kennedy. Read and Witlieb, op.cit., p. 419. Harris, op.cit., p. 175. Edith Green (1910-1987) served as a U.S. Representative from Oregon from 1955-1974. She is reported to have left a substantial legacy in the U.S. Congress. She left her mark on almost every education bill enacted during her tenure. Green supported federal aid to education and the anti-poverty programs of the Great Society while resisting expansion of the federal bureaucracy. She was appointed to the Committee on Education and Labor in her freshman term in the House of Representatives where she served until her final term in the House when she took a seat on the Committee on Appropriations. As chair of the Education and Labor subcommittee on higher education, she was responsible for establishing the first federal program for undergraduate scholarships. "Edith Starrett Green," www.clerkweb.house/gov/womenbio/ExtendedBio/Green_edexb.htm, accessed July 21, 2000, p. 1.

26. Baer, Judith A., *Women in American Law: The Struggle Toward Equality From the New Deal to the Present*, 2nd Edition, New York: Homes & Meier, 1996, p. 80. Harris, op.cit., pp. 175-176.

27. Tobias, Sheila, *Faces of Feminism: An Activist's Reflections on the*

Women's Movement, Boulder, Colorado: Westview Press, 1997, p. 104.

    28. Ibid., p. 105.

    29. Harris, op.cit., p. 176.

    30. Lucena, op.cit., pp. 187-188. "For Engineering Education, 1997 Outputs Look Like 1996," Engineers. *Engineering Workforce Commission of the American Association of Engineering Societies,* Volume 4, Number 1, January 1998, p. 12.

Women Graduates During the 1960s

Year	B.S.		M.S.		Ph.D.	
	Number	Percent	Number	Percent	Number	Percent
1960	145	0.4	26	0.4	3	0.4
1961	135	0.4	27	0.3	6	0.6
1962	125	0.4	40	0.4	4	0.3
1963	130	0.4	32	0.3	11	0.8
1964	159	0.5	34	0.3	7	0.4
1965	139	0.4	44	0.4	10	0.5
1966	146	0.4	76	0.6	9	0.4
1967	184	0.5	78	0.6	11	0.4
1968	177	0.5	58	0.4	5	0.2
1969	328	0.8	107	0.7	23	0.7

    31. "For Engineering Education . . .," op.cit., p. 12.

Women Graduates During the 1970s

Year	B.S.		M.S.		Ph.D.	
	Number	Percent	Number	Percent	Number	Percent
1970	358	0.8	170	1.1	16	0.4
1971	353	0.8	158	1.0	25	0.7
1972	525	1.2	299	1.7	35	0.9
1973	624	1.4	226	1.3	48	1.3
1974	744	1.8	393	2.5	36	1.1
1975	878	2.3	380	2.4	56	1.8
1976	1376	3.6	557	3.4	56	1.9

1977	1961	4.9	646	3.9	67	2.4
1978	3280	7.1	814	5.0	51	2.0
1979	4716	9.0	890	5.6	61	2.2

32. Tobias, op.cit., p. 123.

33. "Telkes, Maria 1900-1995," www.asu.edu/caed/Backup/ AEDlibrary/libarchives/solar/telkes.html, accessed August 25, 1999. www.swe.org/SWE/Awards,achieve3.htm, accessed September 1, 1999, pp. 19-20. Stanley, Autumn, Mothers and Daughters of Invention: Notes for a Revised History of Technology, New Brunswick, NJ; Rutgers University Press, 1995, pp. 63-64, and 66. Source materials include unpublished documents in the authors' possession.

34. "Grace Hopper 1906 –1992," www.greatwomen.org/ hopper.htm, accessed September 1, 1999. www.swe.org . . ., op.cit., p. 15. "Grace Murray Hopper," The National Medal of Technology, U.S. Department of Commerce. Billings, Charlene W., *Grace Hopper: Navy Admiral and Computer Pioneer*, Hillside, NJ: Enslow Publishers, Inc., 1989, pp. 56-59, 74-77, 97-98. Zuckerman, Laurence, "Think Tank: If There's a Bug in the Etymology, You May Never Get it Out," *The New York Times*, April 22, 2000, p. B-11. Zuckerman reports that Thomas Edison referred to a "bug" in his phonograph as early as 1889. Edison is reported to have defined a bug as "an expression for solving a difficulty, and implying that some imaginary insect has secreted itself inside and is causing all the trouble." Stanley, op.cit., pp. 438-442.

35. "Yvonne Brill," www.witi.org/center/witimuseum/hallo fame/ 1999/ybrill.shtml, accessed February 14, 2001, pp. 1-2. www.swe.org..., op.cit., p. 6. Stanley, op.cit., p. 419.

36. Ambrose, Susan A., Kristin L. Dunkle, Barbara B. Lazarus, Indira Nair and Deborah A. Harkus. *Journeys of Women in Science and Engineering: No Universal Constants*. Philadelphia: Temple University Press, 1997, pp. 154-158. Who's Who in Technology, 7th Edition, New York: Gale Research, Inc., 1995, p. 307. www.swe.org..., op.cit., p. 8. "Dr. Thelma Estrin," www.witi.org/center/witimuseum/hallof-fame/1999/testrin.shtml, accessed February 14, 2001, pp. 1-2. Stanley,

op.cit., pp. 443-447. In 1979, Thelma Estrin was still one of only six women Fellows in IEEE. On accepting the IEEE Centennial Medal in 1984, she said she had "participated in and contributed to the emergence of: biomedical engineering, neuroscience, computer engineering, the information society, and the women's movement."

37. "Award Recipient," www.interact.nsf.gov/MOS/Histrec.nsf/..., accessed February 14, 2001. Ambrose, et.al., op.cit., pp. 105-108. "1999 Nicholson Medal for Humanitarian Service to Mildred S. Dresselhaus MIT, "www.aps.org/praw/nicholso/99wind.html, accessed February. 14, 2001, p. 1. "Mildred S. Dresselhaus—1997 AAAS President," www.aaas.org/communications/inside17.htm, accessed February 14, 2001, pp. 1-2. "Mildred Spiewak Dresselhaus," www.witi.org/center/witimuseum/halloffame/1998/mdresselhau.shtml, accessed February 14, 2001, p. 1. Ortiz, Sallie J., "View From the Inside: Meet Mildred Dresselhaus: New Director of the Office of Science,"www.pnl.gov/energyscience/08-00/inside.htm, accessed February 14, 2001, p. 1. *Who's Who in Technology*, op.cit., p. 275. www.swe.org..., op.cit., pp. 9-10.

Chapter Five: Bridges to the Future

1. Lucena, Juan C., "'Women in Engineering' A History and Politics of a Struggle in the Making of a Statistical Category." Proceedings of the 1999 International Symposium on Technology and Society—Women and Technology: Historical, Societal, and Professional Perspectives, 185-194. New Brunswick, NJ, July 29-31, 1999, p. 188.

2. Ibid. National Science Foundation, Women, Minorities, and Person With Disabilities in Science and Engineering: 1996, Arlington, VA, 1996, (NSF 96-311), p. 1. The quote is from the Science and Engineering Equal Opportunities Act, Section 32(b), Part B of P.L. 96-516, 94 Stat. 3010, as amended by P.L. 99-159.

3. "For Engineering Education, 1997 Outputs Look Like 1996," Engineers. *Engineering Workforce Commission of the American*

Association of Engineering Societies, Volume 4, Number 1, January 1998, p. 12.

Women Graduates During the 1980s

Year	B.S.		M.S.		Ph.D.	
	Number	Percent	Number	Percent	Number	Percent
1980	5,631	9.7	1,086	6.3	88	3.2
1981	6,557	10.4	1,232	6.9	90	3.2
1982	8,140	12.2	1,549	8.4	126	4.4
1983	9,566	13.2	1,796	9.0	142	4.7
1984	10,761	14.0	2,149	10.1	153	4.7
1985	11,516	14.8	2,538	11.3	192	5.7
1986	11,264	14.4	2,745	11.9	246	6.7
1987	11,675	15.4	3,119	12.8	296	7.1
1988	10,920	15.3	3,378	13.2	313	6.8
1989	10,529	15.3	3,585	13.6	440	8.8

4. Lucena, op.cit., pp. 188-190. "The Glass Ceiling & Women in Engineering," Report of the NSPE Women in Engineering Task Force, NSPE Publication, Alexandria, Virginia, 1992, p.3.

5. Lucene, op.cit., p. 190.

6. Tobias, Sheila, *Faces of Feminism: An Activist's Reflections on the Women's Movement,* Boulder, Colorado: Westview Press, 1997, p. 115.

7. Lucena, op.cit., p. 190.

8. "For Engineering Education,...", op.cit., p. 12. "Engineering degree totals slump," *Engineers, Engineering Workforce Commission of the American Association of Engineering Societies,* Volume 5, Number 4, December 1999, pp. 1-2 and 4.

Women Graduates During the 1990s

Year	B.S.		M.S.		Ph.D.	
	Number	Percent	Number	Percent	Number	Percent
1990	10,130	15.4	3,826	14.3	495	9.1
1991	10,016	15.7	4,117	14.8	551	9.7
1992	9,972	15.7	4,414	15.5	592	9.9
1993	10,453	16.1	4,876	15.7	600	9.7
1994	10,800	16.6	5,131	16.1	711	11.0
1995	11,303	17.5	5,381	16.7	802	12.1
1996	11,737	18.0	5,495	17.7	854	12.5
1997	12,160	18.7	5,800	19.0	835	12.2
1998	11,796	18.7	6,125	20.3	810	12.3
1999	12,360	19.8	6,205	20.5	858	14.7

9. The Summit on Women in Engineering. National Academy of Engineering. May 17-18, 1999, Washington, D.C. Program Book. The effort was called the Celebration of Women in Engineering. The web site is www.nae.edu/CWE.

10. *Land of Plenty*, Report of the Congressional Commission on the Advancement of Women and Minorities in Science, Engineering and Technology Development, September 2000, pp. 88-91 and pp. 2-6.

11. "About WEPAN," www.wepan.org/about.html," accessed February 19, 2001. "Welcome to WEPAN," www.wepan.org, accessed February 19, 2001. Wadsworth, Emily M. and William K. LeBold, "Final Report: The 1991 National Survey of Women in Engineering Programs," WEPAN, Working Paper 93-1, January 1993, inside front cover. In 1975, 108 institutions (out of a total of 146 engineering institutions that had women students enrolled) replied to a survey indicating that they had either formal or informal women in engineering program activities. By 1991, 186 institutions out of a total of 293 institutions with women enrolled responded to a survey about women in engineering programs.

12. "NACME: Our Mission & Strategy," www.nacme.org/org.html, accessed February 19, 2001. "NAMEPA, Inc.: Mission Statement," www.namepa.org, accessed February 19, 2001, p.1. "Bill and Melinda

Gates Announce New Millenium Scholars Program to Bridge the Gap in Access to Higher Education," September 16, 1999, www.techresource.org/press/990916statement.html, accessed October 28 ,1999, pp. 1-2. The Bill and Melinda Gates Foundation had an endowment of $17 billion. The program will be administered by the United Negro College Fund with the support and participation of the Hispanic Scholarship Fund and the American Indian College Fund.

13. "Engineering degree totals slump," op.cit., p. 4.

14. 'For Engineering Education...," op.cit., p. 11.

15. "Engineering degree totals slump," op.cit., p. 4. A National Survey of Women and Men Engineers: A Study of the Members of 22 Engineering Societies, Society of Women Engineers, New York, 1993, p. 21.

16. *Women Scientists and Engineers Employed in Industry: Why So Few?* National Research Council, Committee on Women in Science and Engineering, Washington, DC: National Academy Press, 1994, p. 1.

17. "A National Survey . . ." op.cit., pp. 32 and 34.

18. Babco, Eleanor, *Professional Women & Minorities: A Total Human Resources Data Compendium*, Commission on Professionals in Science & Technology, Thirteenth Edition, April 2000, ISSN: 0190-1796, p. 151.

19. Eleven deans of engineering and U.S. universities are identified in an e-mail dated December 7, 2000 from Claire LeBlanc to the WEPAN listserve. The deans are: Eleanor Baum, Cooper Union; Ilene Busch-Vishniac, Johns Hopkins University; Denice Denton, University of Washington; Dianne Dorland, Rowan University; Janie Fouke, Michigan State University; Nancy Jannik, Winona State University; Kristina Johnson, Duke University; Jane Long, University of Nevada-Reno; Linda Lucas, University of Alabama—Birmingham; Stacie Nunes, SUNY—New Paltz; and Zorica Pantic-Tanner, San Francisco State University.

20. "A National Survey..." op.cit., p. 32.

21. "Engineering educators get a raise,"Engineers, Engineering Workforce Commission of the American Association of Engineering Societies, Volume 5, Number 1, March 1999, pp. 1, 3-4.

Engineer Educator Salaries – All Engineering Schools

Rank	Mean Annual Salary
Full Professor	$86,450
Associate Professor	$63,300
Assistant Professor	$57,900
Instructor	$53,350

Average Annual Salaries (1998)

Law and Legal Studies	94,507
Business Management	77,367
Engineering	72,616
Computer & Info. Sciences	70,514
Mathematics	61,117
Psychology	60,010
Architecture	55,213
Engineering-Related Technologies	51,785
Public Administration & Services	45,946

Engineering Annual Salaries (1998)

Engineering, General	83,343
Ocean Engineering	79,899
Nuclear Engineering	79,780
Materials Engineering	78,389
Petroleum Engineering	77,064
Chemical Engineering	76,811
Metallurgical Engineering	76,743
Engineering Mechanics	76,124
Aerospace Engineering	75,362
Electrical & Electronics Engineering	74,649
Engineering, Other	74,134
Surveying Engineering	71,344

Mechanical Engineering	71,317
Environmental/Health Engineering	70,432
Bioengineering	69,955
Industrial/Manufacturing Engineering	69,836
Mining and Mineral Engineering	69,032
Textile Sciences & Engineering	68,531
Civil Engineering, General	68,424
Computer Engineering	68,122
Agricultural Engineering	60,443
Architectural Engineering	57,337

22. Babco, op.cit., p. 115.

23. Lucena, op.cit., p. 190.

24. "Dr. Sheila Widnall," www.witi.com/center/witimuseum/hallof-fame/1996/dwidnall.shtml, accessed December 22, 2000, pp. 1-2. "Sheila E. Widnall, Ph.D.," www.wic.org/bio/swidnall.htm, accessed December 22, 2000. "Dr. Sheila E. Widnall," www.af.mil/news/biographies/widnall_se.html, accessed December 22, 2000, pp. 1-2. "1998 IEEE Medals," *IEEE Spectrum*, June 1998, p. 66. Ambrose, Susan A., Kristin L. Dunkle, Barbara B. Lazarus, Indira Nair and Deborah A. Harkus. *Journeys of Women in Science and Engineering: No Universal Constants.* Philadelphia: Temple University Press, 1997, pp. 422-425. Flowers, Dr. Sandra H., and Micahel H. Abbott, *Women in Aviation and Space*, U.S. Department of Transportation Federal Aviation Administration, undated, p. 8. Widnall holds patent numbers 4,264,290 issued April 28, 1981 (Fiber velocity imparter device for dry-forming systems), 4,276,248 issued June 30, 1981 (Methods for forming fibrous webs), and 5,181,678 issued January 26, 1993 (Flexible tailored elastic airfoil section). Stanley, Autumn, *Mothers and Daughters of Invention: Notes for a Revised History of Technology*, New Brunswick, NJ: Rutgers University Press, 1995, p. 408. *Who's Who in Technology*, 7th Edition, New York: Gale Research, Inc., 1995, p. 1328.

25. "Dr. Eleanor Baum," www.witi.com/center/witimuseum/hallof-fame/previousinducte/1996/dbaum.shtml, accessed July 1, 1999, pp. 1-

2. "Why Outward Bound for Engineers?" www.cooper.edu/engineering/projects/outwardbound/obstory1.html, accessed December 30, 1998, p. 1. "Eleanor Baum," *IEEE Spectrum*, February 1993, pp. 42-44. "Rebel with a cause becomes 1st lady dean of engineering, *The National Enquirer*, June 11, 1991, p. 10. *Who's Who in Technology*, op.cit., p. 73. Ambrose, op.cit., pp. 44-47.

26. Shirley, Donna with Danelle Morton, *Managing Martians*, New York: Broadway Books, 1998. This book is subtitled, "The extraordinary story of a woman's lifelong quest to 'get to Mars'—and of the team behind the space robot that has captured the imagination of the world." Shirley's other book is titled *Managing Creativity: A Practical Guide to Inventing, Developing and Producing Innovative Products.* "Managing Creativity," www.managingcreativity.com/, accessed December 22, 2000. "Managing Creativity," www.donnashirley.com/Shirley.html, accessed December 22, 2000. "Profiles of Women at JPL: Donna Shirley," www.jpl.nasa.gov/tours/women/Shirley.html, accessed December 22, 2000. From Flexner, Eleanor and Ellen Fitzpatrick, *Century of Struggle: The Women's Rights Movement in the United States*, Enlarged Edition, Cambridge, Massachusetts: The Belknap Press of Harvard University, 1996, pp.84-85: Sojourner Truth, born the slave Isabella near Kingston on the Hudson River in New York, became an active abolitionist and woman's rights activist after New York freed its slaves by law in 1827. At a woman's rights convention in Akron, Ohio, Sojourner followed a clergyman who had ridiculed the weakness and helplessness of women who should not be given the right to vote. Her eloquence carried the day and led to her signature phrase "Ain't I a woman?"

> The man over there says women need to be helped into carriages and lifted over ditches, and to have the best place everywhere. Nobody ever helps me into carriages or over puddles, or gives me the best place—and ain't I a woman? Look at my arm! I have ploughed and planted and gathered into barns, and no man could head

me—and ain't I a woman? I could work as much and eat as much as a man—when I could get it—and bear the lash as well! And ain't I a woman? I have born thirteen children, and seen most of 'em sold into slavery, and when I cried out with my mother's grief, none but Jesus heard me—and ain't I am woman? If my cup won't hold but a pint, and yours holds a quart, wouldn't ye be mean not to let me have my little half measure full?

27. "Beyond 2000: Exploring Perspectives," Society of Women Engineers National Conference, Program Book, June 27—July 1, 2000, p. 47. 2000 SWE Achievement Award Nomination Package for Suzanne Jenniches, December 15, 1999.

28. "Judith A. Resnik Award," swww2.ieee.org/about/ awards/sums/resnik.htm, accessed February 14, 2001. Brody, Seymour, "Judith Resnik," www.us-israel.org/jsource/biography/Resnik.html, accessed February 14, 2001, pp. 1-2.

29. "Dr. Bonnie J. Dunbar," www.witi.com/center/witimuseum/ halloffame/2000/bdunbar.shtml, accessed December 22, 2000, pp. 1-2. "Biographical Data," www.jsc.nasa.gov/Bios/htmlbios/dunbar.html, accessed December 22, 2000, pp. 1-2.

30. Tietjen, Jill S., Kristy A. Schloss, Carol Carter, Joyce Bishop, and Sarah Lyman Kravits, *Keys to Engineering Success,* Upper Saddle River, NJ: Prentice Hall, 2001, p. 25. "Sherita T. Ceasar," www.witi.com/center/witimuseum/halloffame/1999/sceasar.shtml, accessed December 22, 2000, pp. 1-2.

Appendix: Types of Engineers

1. Tietjen, Jill S., Kristy A. Schloss, Carol Carter, Joyce Bishop, and Sarah Lyman Kravits, *Keys to Engineering Success,* Upper Saddle River, NJ: Prentice Hall, 2001, Appendix A, pp. 267-270.

Bibliography

Webster's Dictionary of American Women, New York: SMITHMARK Publishers, 1996.

Who's Who in Technology, 7th Edition, New York: Gale Research, Inc., 1995.

Alice, Margaret, *Hypatia's Heritage: A History of Women in Science from Antiquity through the Nineteenth Century*, Boston, Massachusetts: Beacon Press, 1986.

Ambrose, Susan A., Kristin L. Dunkle, Barbara B. Lazarus, Indira Nair and Deborah A. Harkus. *Journeys of Women in Science and Engineering: No Universal Constants*. Philadelphia: Temple University Press, 1997.

Babco, Eleanor, *Professional Women & Minorities: A Total Human Resources Data Compendium*, Commission on Professionals in Science & Technology, Thirteenth Edition, April 2000, ISSN: 0190-1796.

Baer, Judith A., *Women in American Law: The Struggle Toward Equality From the New Deal to the Present*, 2nd Edition, New York: Homes & Meier, 1996.

Barker, Anne M., "Women in Engineering During World War II: A Taste of Victory," November 21, 1994, unpublished, Rochester Institute of Technology.

Bartels, Nancy, "The First Lady of Gearing," www.geartechnology.com/mag/gt-kg.htm, accessed September 2, 1999.

Billings, Charlene W., *Grace Hopper: Navy Admiral and Computer Pioneer*, Hillside, NJ: Enslow Publishers, Inc., 1989.

Bix, Amy Sue, "Engineeresses Invade Campus: Four Decades of Debate over Technical Coeducation," Proceedings of the 1999 International Symposium on Technology and Society—Women and Technology: Historical, Societal, and Professional Perspectives, 195-201, New Brunswick, NJ, July 29-31, 1999.

Brody, Seymour, "Judith Resnik," www.us-israel.org/jsource/biography/Resnik.html, accessed February 14, 2001

Candee, Margorie Dent, Editor, *Current Biography*, New York, NY: The H. W. Wilson Company, 1957.

Dexter, Elizabeth Anthony, *Career Women of America: 1776-1840*, Francetown, New Hampshire: Marshall Jones Company, 1950.

Flexner, Eleanor and Ellen Fitzpatrick, *Century of Struggle: The Women's Rights Movement in the United States*, Enlarged Edition, Cambridge, Massachusetts: The Belknap Press of Harvard University, 1996.

Flowers, Dr. Sandra H., and Micahel H. Abbott, Women in Aviation and Space, U.S. Department of Transportation Federal Aviation Administration, undated.

Garza, Hedda, *Barred From the Bar: A History of Women in the Legal Profession*, New York: Franklin Watts, 1996.

Gilbreth, Frank B., Jr. and Ernestine Gilbreth Carey, *Time Out for Happiness*, New York, NY: Thomas Y. Crowell Company, 1970.

Goff, Alice C., *Women Can Be Engineers*, Ann Arbor, Michigan: Edwards Brothers, Inc., 1946.

Harris, Barbara, *Beyond Her Sphere: Women in the Professions in American History*, Westport, Connecticut: Greenwood Press, 1978.

Huckenpahler, Helen and Donald Morgan, "Women of the Orange Tassel," *Colorado Engineer*, March 1958, pp. 14-55 and ff.

Ingels, Margaret, "Petticoats and Slide Rules," *Western Society of Engineers*, September 4, 1952, and later published in *Midwest Engineer.*

Kass-Simon, G., and Patricia Farnes, Editors, *Women of Science: Righting the Record*, Bloomington, Indiana: Indiana University Press, 1990.

Kindya, Marta Navia, *Four Decades of the Society of Women Engineers*, New York: Society of Women Engineers, 1990.

Koerner, Brendan I., "Where the Boys Aren't," *U.S. News & World Report*, February 8, 1999, pp. 46-55.

LeBold, William K. and Dona J. LeBold, "Women Engineers: A Historical Perspective," *ASEE Prism*, March 1998, pp. 30 - 32.

Lee, Erma Conkling, Editor, *The Biographical Cyclopaedia of American Women*, New York: The Franklin W. Lee Publishing Company, Volume II, 1925.

Lucena, Juan C., "'Women in Engineering' "A History and Politics of a Struggle in the Making of a Statistical Category." Proceedings of the 1999 International Symposium on Technology and Society—Women and Technology: Historical, Societal, and Professional Perspectives, 185-194. New Brunswick, NJ, July 29-31, 1999.

Meade, Jeff, "Ahead of Their Time: A Century Ago, Women Engineers Such as the Brilliant Bertha Lamme Blazed a Lonely Trail," *ASEE Prism*, January 1993, pp. 26-29.

Morrow, Charlene and Teri Perl, Editors, *Notable Women in Mathematics: A Biographical Dictionary*, Westport, Connecticut: Greenwood Press, 1998.

National Science Foundation, *Women, Minorities, and Person With Disabilities in Science and Engineering: 1996*, Arlington, VA, 1996, (NSF 96-311).

Oglivie, Marilyn Bailey, *Women in Science: Antiquity through the Nineteenth Century, a Biographical Dictionary with Annotated Bibliography*, Cambridge, Massachusetts: MIT Press, 1993.

Ortiz, Sallie J., "View From the Inside: Meet Mildred Dresselhaus: New Director of the Office of Science,"www.pnl.gov/energyscience/08-00/inside.htm, accessed February 14, 2001.

Perusek, Anne, "The First Lady of Engineering," *SWE: Magazine of the Society of Women Engineers*, January/February 2000, pp. 82-92.

Read, Phyllis J., and Bernard L. Witlieb, *The Book of Women's Firsts*, New York: Random House, 1992.

Rossiter, Margaret W., *Women Scientists in America: Struggles and Strategies to 1940*, Baltimore, Maryland: The Johns Hopkins University Press, 1992.

Rossiter, Margaret W., *Women Scientists in America: Before Affirmative Action 1940-1972*, Baltimore, Maryland: The Johns Hopkins University Press, 1995.

Schneider, Dorothy and Carl F. Schneider, *The ABC-CLIO Companion to Women in the Workplace*, Santa Barbara, California: ABC-CLIO, Inc., 1993.

Shearer, Benjamin F. and Barbara S. Shearer, Editors, *Notable Women in the Physical Sciences*, Westport, Connecticut: Greenwood Press, 1997.

Shirley, Donna with Danelle Morton, *Managing Martians*, New York: Broadway Books, 1998.

Skinner, Richard A. and G. Phillip Cartwright, "Higher Education and the Technology Workforce Shortage," www.contract.kent.edu/change/articles/mayjun98.html, accessed September 15, 2000.

Stanley, Autumn, *Mothers and Daughters of Invention: Notes for a Revised History of Technology*, New Brunswick, NJ: Rutgers University Press, 1995.

Tietjen, Jill S., Kristy A. Schloss, Carol Carter, Joyce Bishop, and Sarah Lyman Kravits, *Keys to Engineering Success*, Upper Saddle River, NJ: Prentice Hall, 2001.

Tobias, Sheila, *Faces of Feminism: An Activist's Reflections on the Women's Movement*, Boulder, Colorado: Westview Press, 1997.

Turner, Edna May, "Education of Women for Engineering in the United States 1885-1952," (dissertation, New York University, 1954), Ann Arbor, Michigan: UMI Dissertation Services.

Wadsworth, Emily M. and William K. LeBold, "Final Report: The 1991 National Survey of Women in Engineering Programs," WEPAN, Working Paper 93-1, January 1993.

Weigold, Marilyn, *Silent Builder: Emily Warren Roebling and the Brooklyn Bridge*, Port Washington, NY: Associated Faculty Press, Inc., 1984.

Wolfson, Richard and Jay M. Pasachoff, *Physics*, Boston, Massachusetts: Little, Brown and Company, 1987.

Wright, Kenneth R., Jonathan M. Kelly, Alfredo Valencia Zegarra, "Machu Picchu: Ancient Hydraulic Engineering," *Journal of Hydraulic Engineering*, October 1997, pp. 838-843.

Zuckerman, Laurence, "Think Tank: If There's a Bug in the Etymology, You May Never Get It Out," *The New York Times*, April 22, 2000, p. B-11.

"150 People Who Shaped the Way We Live," *The Baltimore Sun 150th Anniversary Publication*, May 17, 1987, p. 184.

"150 Years of Civil Engineering," www.asce.org/150/1506years.html, accessed December 15, 2000.

"1998 IEEE Medals," *IEEE Spectrum*, June 1998, p. 66.

"1999 Nicholson Medal for Humanitarian Service to Mildred S. Dresselhaus MIT, "www.aps.org/praw/nicholso/99wind.html, accessed February 14, 2001.

2000 SWE Achievement Award Nomination Package for Suzanne Jenniches, December 15, 1999.

"About the NAE, www.nae.edu/nae/naehome.nsf/weblinks/NAEW-4NHMQM?opendocument, accessed December 19, 2000.

"About WEPAN," www.wepan.org/about.html," accessed February 19, 2001.

"Again Heads Women Engineers," *The New York Times*, August 6, 1951, p. 14.

"All About the Great Wall of China," www.enchantedlearning.com/subjects/greatwall/Allabout.html, accessed September 26, 2000.

"American Perspectives on Engineers & Engineering." A "Harris Poll" Pilot Study conducted for the American Association of Engineering Societies, July 1998.

"ASCE Profile," www.asce.org/aboutasce/profile.html, accessed December 15, 2000.

"Award Recipient," www.interact.nsf.gov/MOS/Histrec.nsf/. . ., accessed February 14, 2001.

"Beyond 2000: Exploring Perspectives," Society of Women Engineers National Conference, Program Book, June 27 – July 1, 2000.

"Bill and Melinda Gates Announce New Millenium Scholars Program to Bridge the Gap in Access to Higher Education," September 16, 1999, www.techresource.org/press/990916statement.html, accessed October 28, 1999.

"Biographical Data," www.jsc.nasa.gov/Bios/htmlbios/dunbar.html, accessed December 22, 2000.

"Dr. Bonnie J. Dunbar," www.witi.com/center/witimuseum/hallof fame/2000/bdunbar.shtml, accessed December 22, 2000.

"A brief history of AIChE," www.aiche.org/welcome/history.htm, accessed August 20, 1999.

"Brief History of Women at CSM," www.mines.edu/Academic/affairs/ wisem/history1.html, accessed December 20, 2000.

"Daniel Bernoulli and the making of the fluid equation," http://pass.maths.org.uk/issue1/bern/index.html, accessed July 1, 1999.

Design Patent 72,763, United States Patent Office, Patented May 31, 1927.

"Edith Starrett Green," www.clerkweb.house/gov/womenbio/ ExtendedBio/Green_edexb.htm, accessed July 21, 2000.

"Eleanor Baum," *IEEE Spectrum*, February 1993, pp. 42-44.

"Dr. Eleanor Baum: Dean of Engineering Cooper Union Engineering School," www.witi.com/center/witimuseum/halloffame/ previousinducte/1996/dbaum.shtml, accessed July 1, 1999.

"Elizabeth "Elsie" MacGill 1905-1980,"www.corpserve.nrc.ca.corpserve/ hall/u_il4_e.html, accessed December 21, 2000.

"Elizabeth M.G. MacGill," http://collections.ic.gc.ca/high_flyers/ macgill.htm, accessed December 21,2000.

"Ellen Richards," www.greatwomen.org/rchrdse.htm, accessed May 26, 1999.

"Elsie Eaves – Pioneer from the West," SWE Newsletter, May 1959, p. 3.

"Elsie Eaves: Woman Wins Praise in Man's World," *The Colorado Alumnus*, May 1963, p. 8.

"Elsie Eaves Scores Again: Is First Woman Honored with ASCE Life Membership," McGraw-Hill News-Bulletin, March 15, 1962, p. 6.

"Elsie MacGill," www.ontario2000.on.ca./engl. . .eatmoments/ scitech/macgill_sum.htm, accessed December 21, 2000.

Employment Opportunities for Women in Professional Engineering, Women's Bureau Bulletin No. 254, Washington, DC: U.S. Government Printing Office, 1954.

"Engineering Degrees, 1996: Numbers of Women, Minority Graduates Reach All-Time Highs," *Engineers: A Quarterly Bulletin on Careers in the Profession*, Engineering Workforce Commission of the American Association of Engineering Societies, Volume 3, Number 1, January 1997, pp. 3-8.

"Engineering degree totals slump," Engineers, *Engineering Workforce Commission of the American Association of Engineering Societies,* Volume 5, Number 4, December 1999, pp. 1-2, 4, and 6.

"Engineering educators get a raise," Engineers, *Engineering Workforce Commission of the American Association of Engineering Societies,* Volume 5, Number 1, March 1999, pp. 1, 3-4.

"Engineers of the Future," *San Francisco Chronicle,* February 26, 1999, page A26.

"For Engineering Education, 1997 Outputs Look Like 1996," *Engineers. Engineering Workforce Commission of the American Association of Engineering Societies,* Volume 4, Number 1, January 1998, pp. 9-13.

"Founder Societies of the United Engineering Foundation," www.uefoundation.org/fndsoc.html, accessed December 15, 2000.

"A Gallery of Electromagnetic Personalities," www.ee.umd.edu/~tay lor/frame8.htm, frame3.htm, frame4.htm, and frame7.htm, accessed July 1, 1999.

"General Information About SWE—Society of Women Engineers," www.swe.org/SWE/Atlarge/swe_info.htm#origins, accessed September 1, 1999.

"The Glass Ceiling & Women in Engineering," *Report of the NSPE Women in Engineering Task Force,* NSPE Publication, Alexandria, Virginia, 1992.

"Grace Hopper 1906 –1992," www.greatwomen.org/hopper.htm, accessed September 1, 1999.

"Grace Murray Hopper," The National Medal of Technology, U.S. Department of Commerce.

"Grand Canal (Italy)," http://Encarta.msn.com/index/conciseindex/, accessed September 26, 2000.

"Harris Poll Show Engineering Remains a 'Stealth Profession' Among Women and Minorities," Press Release, American Association of Engineering Societies, September 1, 1998.

"Historical Highlights," www.idis.com/aime/history.htm, accessed December 15, 2000.

"The History of ASME International," www.asme.org/history /asmehist.html, accessed December 15, 2000.

"Judith A. Resnik Award," swww2.ieee.org/about/awards/sums/ resnik.htm, accessed February 14, 2001.

"The Land Grant System of Education in the United States," http://www.ag.ohio.state.edu/~ ohioline/lines/lgrant.html, accessed April 11, 2000.

"Landmarks of the World: Brooklyn Bridge," *Holiday*, June 1959, The Curtis Publishing Company.

"Land of Plenty," Report of the Congressional Commission on the Advancement of Women and Minorities in Science, Engineering and Technology Development, September 2000.

"Managing Creativity," www.managingcreativity.com/, accessed December 22, 2000.

"Managing Creativity," www.donnashirley.com/Shirley.html, accessed December 22, 2000.

"Mildred S. Dresselhaus – 1997 AAAS President," www.aaas.org/communications/inside17.htm, accessed February 14, 2001.

"Mildred Spiewak Dresselhaus," www.witi.org/center/witimuseum/halloffame/1998/mdresselhau.shtml, accessed February 14, 2001.

"NACME: Our Mission & Strategy," www.nacme.org/org.html, accessed February 19, 2001.

"NAMEPA, Inc.: Mission Statement," www.namepa.org, accessed February 19, 2001.

A National Survey of Women and Men Engineers: A Study of the Members of 22 Engineering Societies, Society of Women Engineers, New York, 1993.

"New Mexico State University College of Agriculture and Home Economics," accessed September 15, 2000.

"Nominations accepted for prestigious Hoover Medal," ASMENEWS, www.asmenews.org/features/hoover.html, accessed December 20, 2000.

"Number of women studying engineering still growing," Engineers, Engineering Workforce Commission of the American Association of Engineering Societies, Volume 5, Number 2, June 1999, page 4.

"The Origins of IEEE," www.ieee.org/organizations/. . .ical_articles/history_of_ieee.html, accessed December 15, 2000.

The Outlook for Women in Architecture and Engineering, Bulletin of the Women's Bureau No. 223-5, Washington, DC: U.S. Government Printing Office, 1948.

"An Overview of the United Engineering Foundation: History," www.uefoundation.org/overview.html, accessed December 15, 2000.

"Past Hoover Medal Recipients," www.asme.org/member/awards/ hoover_medal/past.html, accessed December 20, 2000.

Patent 1,693,108, United States Patent Office, Patented November 27, 1928.

"The Phi Beta Kappa Society: A Short History of Phi Beta Kappa," www.pbk.org/history.htm, accessed December 19, 2000

"Profiles of Women at JPL: Donna Shirley," www.jpl.nasa.gov/ tours/women/Shirley.html, accessed December 22, 2000.

"Rebel with a cause becomes 1st lady dean of engineering," *The National Enquirer,* June 11, 1991, p. 10.

"Rediscover Ancient Egypt with Tehuti Research Foundation," www.Egypt-tehuti.com/phyramids.html, accessed September 26, 2000.

"Sheila E. Widnall, Ph.D.," www.wic.org/bio/swidnall.htm, accessed December 22, 2000.

"Dr. Sheila Widnall," www.witi.com/center/witimuseum/hallof fame/1996/dwidnall.shtml, accessed December 22, 2000.

"Dr. Sheila E. Widnall," www.af.mil/news/biographies/widnall_se.html, accessed December 22, 2000.

"Sherita T. Ceasar," www.witi.com/center/witimuseum/hallof fame/1999/sceasar.shtml, accessed December 22, 2000.

"Sir Isaac Newton and Chronology," www.reformation.org/Newton.html, accessed July 1, 1999.

Society History," www.asse.org/hsoci.htm, accessed December 19, 2000.

The Summit on Women in Engineering. National Academy of Engineering. May 17-18, 1999, Washington, D.C. Program Book.

"SWE's first fellow members: their achievements and careers," *U.S. Woman Engineer*, December 1980, p. 9.

"Tau Beta Pi: Integrity and Excellence in Engineering," www.tbp.org, accessed August 20, 1999.

"Telkes, Maria 1900-1995," www.asu.edu/caed/Backup/AEDlibrary /libarchives/solar/telkes.html, accessed August 25, 1999.

"Tesla, Nikola,"www.neuronet.pitt.edu/~ bogdan/tesla/bio.htm, accessed July 1, 1999.

"Dr. Thelma Estrin," www.witi.org/center/witimuseum/hallof fame/1999/testrin.shtml, accessed February 14, 2001.

"U.S. Agencies Seek Women Engineers," *The New York Times*, March 12, 1951, p. 19.

"WAAIME," www.idis.com/aime/WAAIME.HTM, accessed December 19, 2000.

"Welcome to the IEEE Fellow Program: Our History," www.ieee.org/about/awards/fellows/fellows.htm, accessed December 19, 2000.

"Welcome to WEPAN," www.wepan.org, accessed February 19, 2001.

"Why Outward Bound for Engineers?" www.cooper.edu/engineering/ projects/outwardbound/obstory1.html, accessed December 30, 1998.

"Women Could Fill Engineering Jobs: Trade Society, Meeting Here, Told They Represent Untapped 'Source of Qualified Talent,'" *The New York Times*, March 16, 1952, p. 79.

"Women Engineers See Field Widening," *The New York Times*, March 11, 1951, p. 47.

Women Scientists and Engineers Employed in Industry: Why So Few? National Research Council, Committee on Women in Science and Engineering, Washington, DC: National Academy Press, 1994.

"Yvonne Brill," www.witi.org/center/witimuseum/halloffame/ 1999/ybrill.shtml, accessed February 14, 2001.

www.iienet.org/Aboutg.htm, accessed August 20, 1999.

www.iienet.org/historg.htm, accessed August 20, 1999.

www.swe.org/SWE/Awards,achieve3.htm, accessed September 1, 1999.

www.tbp.org/TBP/INFORMATION/Info_book/membership, accessed
    August 20, 1999.

Index